The Glacier Mummy

otzishop.com
ÖTZI
Der Mann aus dem Eis
L'uoma venuto dal ghiaccio
The iceman

Gudrun Sulzenbacher

The Glacier Mummy

Discovering the Neolithic Age with the **Iceman**

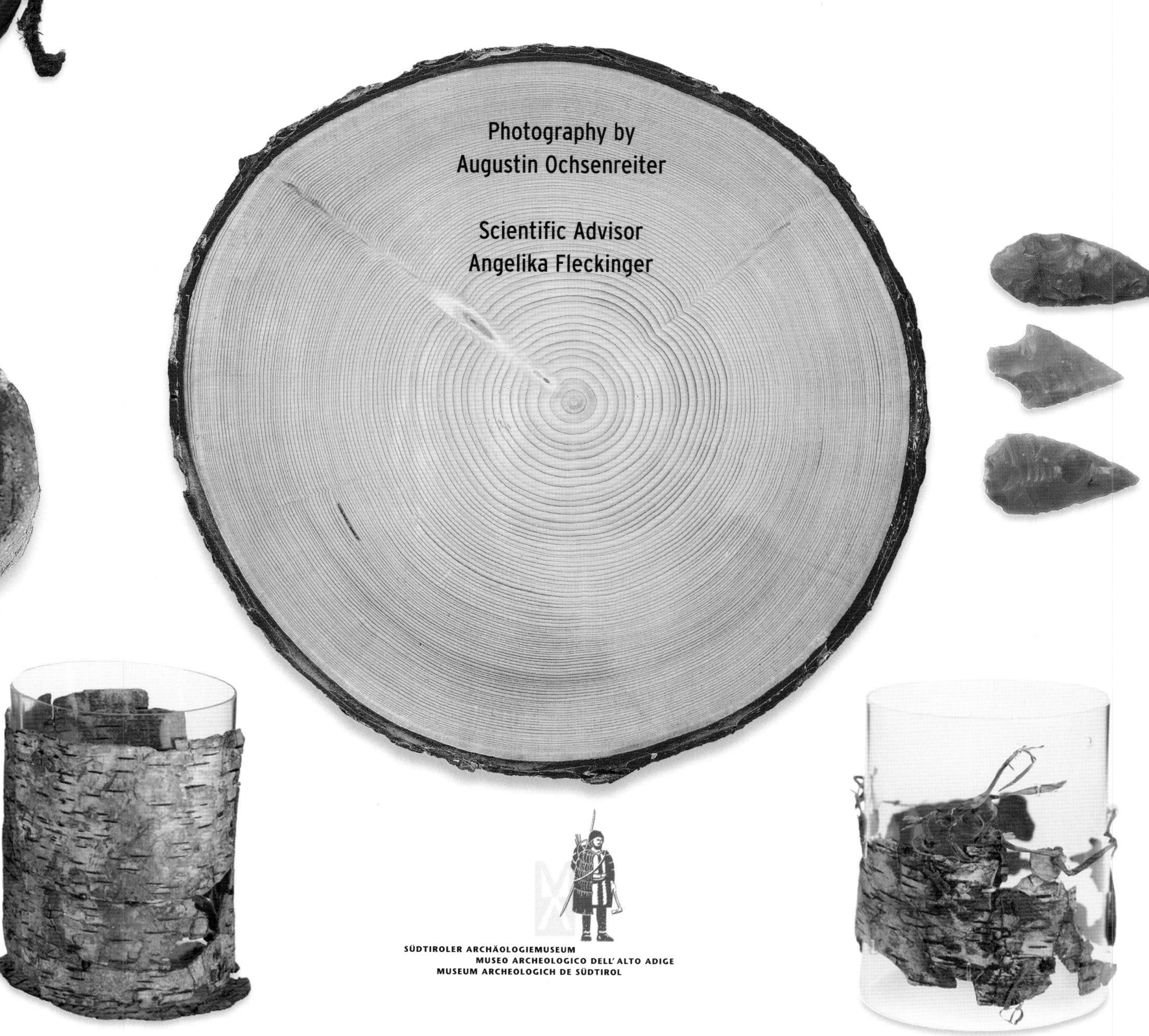

Folio

Thanks

Martin Andres, Sigmar Bortenschlager, Maddalena Braccesi, Luigi Capasso, Matthäus Desaler, Eduard Egarter Vigl, Markus Egg, Luis Egger, Maria Egger, Renato Fasolo, Pizzeria Feldheim, Brenda Fowler, Stefan Galler, Salon Hanni, Wulf Hein, Ernst Hofer, Günther Hofer, Hansjörg Hofer, Ariano Maestri, Helmuth Mahlknecht, Gerlind Mailler, Stephanie Mich, Massimo Morpurgo, Maria Oberrauch, Peter Oberrauch, Christine Ochsenreiter, Klaus Oeggl, Johannes Pan, Linde Pattis, Joris Peters, Joe Pfeifer, Jean-Loup Ringot, Marco Samadelli, Alex Sanin, Schullian market garden, Wolfgang Sölder, Ester Solderer, Stampfl butcher's shop, Oswald Stimpfl, Gislar Sulzenbacher, Josef Sulzenbacher, Veronika Tauber, Umberto Tecchiati, Martin Zelger and the pedagogical unit of the South Tyrol Museum of Archaeology have all contributed to the making of this book in an enormous variety of ways - as enthusiastic Stone Age experts, meticulous specialists, photo models, assiduous material and picture researchers and above all, in the exhaustive search, collection and preparation of photographic objects: fresh flowers, wild berries, naturally occurring fruit, rare tree fungus, dried lumps of tree resin, polished timber, American magazines and other artefacts of the most diverse nature. Special thanks go to all of them.

South Tyrol Museum of Archaeology
www.iceman.it

Second updated edition 2006

Translation: Geraint Williams
Graphic design: no.parking, Vicenza
Photolithography and printing: Lanarepro, Lana
ISBN-10: 3-85256-199-X
ISBN-13: 978-3-85256-199-8

www.folioverlag.com

Contents

The Find of the Century

Around 5,300 years ago, a man was travelling through the Ötz Valley in the Alps with damaged equipment and without food. High up in the icy mountains he met his death. Thousands of years later he was excavated from the ice as a deep-frozen mummy and became known all over the world by the nickname "Ötzi", after the valley where he was found. On September 19, 1991, the melted ice of the glacier revealed what it had conserved for millennia – not only the man's body but also his equipment and items of his clothing. Had Ötzi died beneath the level of the glacier, his body and possessions would not have been frozen but more likely eaten by wild animals. At best only pieces of copper and flint would have survived. These artefacts give us a fascinating picture of life in the Neolithic or Late Stone Age and represent the unique feature of the discovery of the Iceman.

UNFINISHED
Ötzi's half-finished bow, carefully propped up to the right of the stone slab where he lay, remained undisturbed for thousands of years. The lower part was firmly stuck half a metre deep in the ice. As it was impossible to remove, the visible part was simply broken off. The remaining piece was finally extracted during the second round of excavations in summer 1992.

THE MONUMENT
Today a four-metre-high stone pyramid marks the spot on the Tisenjoch where the Glacier Mummy was found.

Restored bow

THE DISCOVERERS
On descending from the Finail peak towards the Similaun refuge, Erika and Helmut Simon, a couple from Nuremberg, Germany, were shocked to discover a corpse. They took it to be an unfortunate mountain climber who had died maybe ten or twenty years earlier.

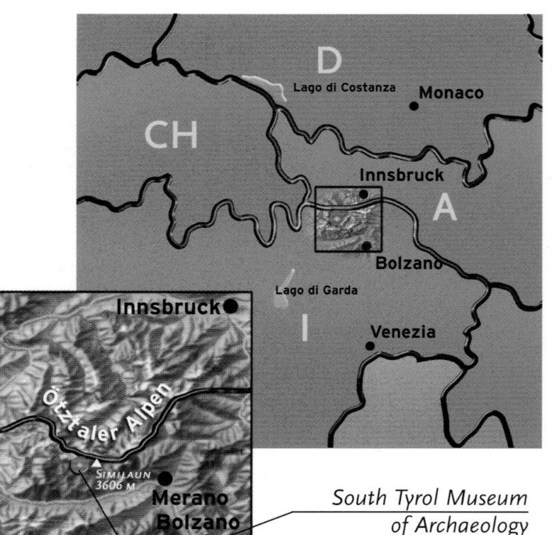

South Tyrol Museum of Archaeology

Location of the find

WHERE WAS ÖTZI FOUND?
The Iceman was found in the Ötz Alps, a mountain range between Italy and Austria. He lay directly on the border between the two countries but later measurements showed that his body was in fact discovered on Italian territory.

TOO LATE TO REPAIR
Around five metres away from the mummy lay Ötzi's quiver, looking just as it did over 5,000 years ago when it froze on the stony ground. It came to light the day after the Iceman was taken away. The wooden rod that supported the chamois quiver was broken into three pieces, the middle section having been excavated along with the mummy. Ötzi was probably carrying this piece in his pocket in order to repair it.

SURPRISINGLY SMALL

On Ötzi's right hip hung a small dagger in an elaborate sheath made of plaited lime bast. Both objects were damaged by blows of an ice pick during the extraction of the corpse from the ice. However the tip of the dagger had already been broken.

THE LOCATION OF THE FIND

Ötzi's icy grave is located at 3,210 metres above sea level near the summer path from the Similaun refuge to the Tisenjoch ridge, around 73 metres below the latter. As Tisenjoch does not appear on official maps, the authorities chose the scientific designation of Ötzi's grave as the nearest official geographic point: the Hauslabjoch glacier. This ridge is around 330 metres from the location of the find and forms the crossing point from the Ötz Valley into the Senales Valley.

SHOES

The mummy's right shoe is in the best state of conservation and remained on his foot when Ötzi was excavated.

NEOLITHIC RUCKSACK?

Along with the bow and arrows, many other pieces of wood came to light including a U-shaped hazel stick and remains of string and hide. Together these items probably formed a carrying frame to which a bag was attached with string.

A ROUTINE CORPSE

This is one of the first photos of the Iceman, as he lay on the stone slab, his face obscured. He was first thought to be the victim of a mountaineering accident in 1938 and therefore a routine case for forensic medicine.

WHO THE CAP FITS?

Ötzi's fur cap was discovered by archaeologists during the second round of excavations in the summer of 1992. Lying at the foot of the stone slab where Ötzi was found, the chin straps had been torn before his death.

TRAMPLED UNDERFOOT

Ötzi carried two cylindrical containers made of birch bark. One of them lay beside the mummy's head and was immediately noticed by Mr and Mrs Simon. Two days later however, it was carelessly crushed underfoot.

A PECULIAR PICKAXE

The unique prehistoric hatchet was originally thought to be a pickaxe and taken away by the police as evidence. After the official excavation of the Iceman, it provided decisive information for the calculation of Ötzi's age.

Longbow

The Recovery

On the day after Ötzi's discovery nobody could have imagined that this would turn out to be the archaeological find of the century or the publicity it would later attract. The first recovery attempt was a failure as the lower part of the corpse was stuck hard in the ice. Repeated slips of the pneumatic drill bore deep into the Iceman's flesh and soon after the compressor ran out of electricity. The corpse was finally freed from the ice four days after the discovery. Along with the corpse came wooden objects, pieces of hide and grass knots which created further puzzles. Rumours started to circulate that the corpse displayed a head wound, had burn marks on the back and that it had even been tied up. Legal proceedings were undertaken and the Iceman became a case for the public prosecutor and forensic medicine.

"ÖTZI" - A NICKNAME

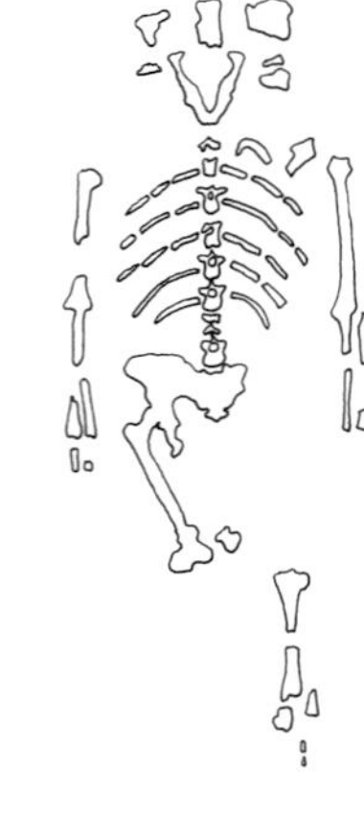

While the Glacier Mummy was called "Frozen Fritz" in America and "Hibernatus" in France, the name "Ötzi", first coined by a Vienna journalist on September 26, 1991, appears to be the most popular worldwide. Apart from Ötzi, only two examples of human remains have been given nicknames: in 1976, a 3-million-year-old skeleton of a female Australopithecus found in Ethiopia was baptised "Lucy" as the Beatles' song "Lucy in The Sky with Diamonds" was playing on the archaeologists' cassette player at the time. The other case is "Juanita", the mummified corpse of an Inca girl found in Peru in 1995 and officially known as the "Ice Maiden".

AIR TRANSPORT

The Iceman was flown to Vent in the Ötz Valley in a helicopter belonging to the Austrian Ministry of the Interior.

AFTER THE FIRST RECOVERY ATTEMPT

On Friday September 20, the melting snow revealed a further 10cm of the corpse. It could therefore be calculated that the corpse had been exposed to the light for some three days before its discovery.

CAUGHT ON FILM

On Monday September 23, 1991, the mummy was finally removed from the ice. That day, forensic doctors from Innsbruck University were flown to the scene without extraction tools, thinking that the corpse had already been free from the ice. However, during the night of Sunday to Monday, the corpse had frozen in again and so the experts decided to use icepicks and ski sticks borrowed from mountaineers in order to cut Ötzi free. Their work was captured on film by a team from Austrian state television. These images caused a sensation around the world and provided important documentary footage of the extraction since as yet no archaeologists had been present.

BRISK BUSINESS

On the weekend before the recovery, crowds of onlookers inundated the scene of the find, chipping away at the ice, taking photos and even removing objects. Among the most famous visitors were the rock climbers Reinhold Messner and Hans Kammerlander. Alois Pirpamer, father of the keeper of the nearby Similaun refuge, prepared the mummy for its transport to Innsbruck.

Similaun refuge in summer 1992

STIFF AND AWKWARD - SNAP!

On exposing the mummy, numerous pieces of leather and hide, string, straps and tufts of hay as well as a dagger with a flint blade and wooden handle were discovered. These objects, along with the leathery corpse, were packed in a plastic sack and flown by helicopter to the town of Vent in the Ötz Valley. There the corpse was placed in a coffin - during which Ötzi's left arm was snapped off - and driven in a hearse to the Institute of Forensic Medicine of Innsbruck University and given the serial number 91/619: corpse Hauslabjoch.

MUMMY IN THE MEDIA

The Iceman quickly embarked on a meteoric media career. Journalists stormed the offices of academics and newspapers worldwide and speculated wildly on the life and death of the Glacier Mummy. A TV journalist even reported that Ötzi was in fact an Egyptian or Peruvian mummy which a hoaxer had deposited on the Hauslabjoch.

Austrian Police
Italian customs police officer

92 METRES AND 56 CENTIMETRES

A new survey of the boundary line between the two countries revealed that Ötzi lay a few metres over the Austrian border on Italian territory. The South Tyrolean authorities entrusted the ownership rights to Innsbruck University in order to facilitate the scientific examination of the Iceman.

VITAMINS

Two Innsbruck archaeologists came across a sloe berry at the scene of the find on September 27.

Restored quiver strut

A CRUCIAL CLUE?

On September 25, researchers on the glacier discovered Ötzi's quiver. It had first appeared sticking out of the ice the previous day. Meanwhile the central section of the supporting strut had already been at Innsbruck University for two days.

Fully intact right shoe

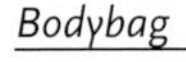

Bodybag

A MYSTERY

The retoucheur - one of Ötzi's tools - resembles a thick pencil stub. Nothing of its kind had ever been seen before. At first archaeologists took it to be a flint fire starter before scientific examination solved the riddle of its real function.

SENSATION!

On September 24, the Glacier Mummy was examined by an archaeologist for the first time. The ancient historian Konrad Spindler immediately estimated Ötzi's age to be "at least 4000 years old" and came up against a wall of disbelief. Reporters soon appeared and the first pictures of Ötzi began to circulate around the world. Here was a sensation in the making!

SUPPORT FROM THE SUN

At the scene of the find, Ötzi's right foot lay over the left. The bright September sunshine helped to expose the mummy. As the left foot was anchored more deeply in the ice and therefore much more difficult to extract, the left shoe is far more damaged than the right.

Excavations in the Glacier

UNFAMILIAR CONDITIONS
Up to this point, archaeologists had always carried out their research in the earth under normal atmospheric conditions. Now they were forced to struggle in the Alpine ice with the aid of steam and drying apparatus.

Now it was the turn of the archaeologists to find answers to countless questions: is the piece of wood really a part of a bow? If so, where was the bow string? Why was Ötzi's quiver already damaged before his death? What was the function of this small, pencil-like tool with the stubby point? And who indeed was this man? Why had he climbed so high up into the mountains, how did he die and what happened to him during his lifetime? When they undertake excavations, archaeologists slowly feel their way back into the past and search for scattered clues in order to reconstruct a picture, rather like piecing together a jigsaw. After Ötzi was recovered from the ice, two scientific expeditions were sent to the Tisenjoch to survey the scene, reconstruct the location of the finds and search for further objects. In doing so, the experts were confronted with some unusual circumstances.

WELL-PRESERVED
The outstanding find of the summer of 1992 was Ötzi's bearskin cap. Unlike the other garments, the cap was in an excellent state of conservation. Moments later, Ötzi's broken bow-stave was unearthed.

COLD AND WET
The water in the rocky hollow where Ötzi lay was drained off and repeatedly sieved and filtered.

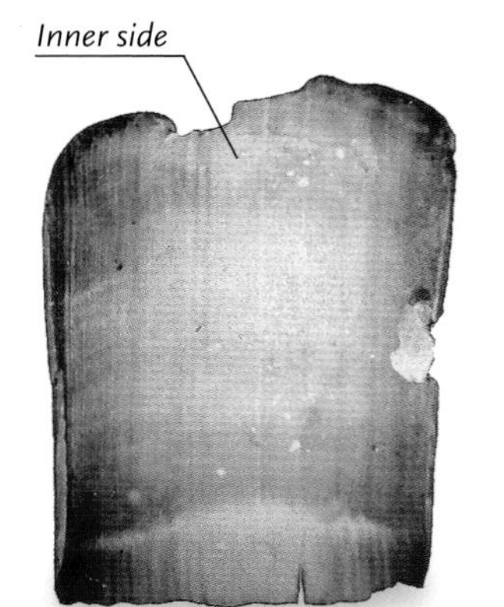

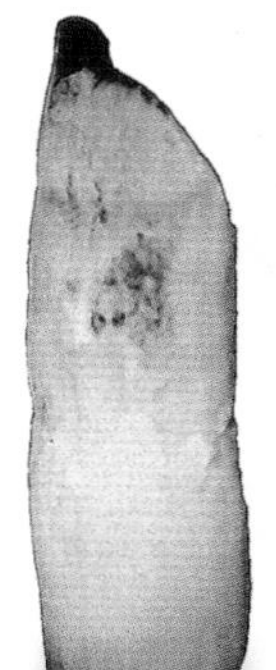

PRECIOUS LITTLE FINDS
Several of Ötzi's fingernails and toenails were missing. One fingernail was found during the second excavation in summer 1992, while three of his toenails appeared during the restoration of his left shoe at the Römisch-Germanisches Zentralmuseum in Mainz, Germany.

SHOULDER-LENGTH HAIR
Hairs found in 1992 on or beside the stone slab where Ötzi lay were up to nine centimetres long.

FINE FILTERS
By using these special sieves, the experts were able to isolate the tiniest particles of animal, plant and human remains.

PANNING FOR GOLD
Grass, moss, leaves, charcoal particles, hair and parts of insects were filtered out. From the muddy floor of the channel out of the hollow came pieces of skin, muscle fibres, blood vessels and a fingernail. Some of these remains came from the hip wound Ötzi sustained during the first unsuccessful attempt to remove him from the ice.

THE SECOND "MAJOR" EXCAVATION

In mid-summer 1992, the scene of the find was thoroughly investigated over a period of a month. Despite the fine weather, there was still a two-metre-thick layer of snow over the rocky gully. In a summer like this Ötzi would never have been discovered.

Similaun Peak

THE FIRST EXCAVATION

At the beginning of October 1991, shortly after Ötzi's recovery, investigators found the remains of some grass matting, other pieces of leather and hide, sections of a birch-bark container and its contents, string and pieces of wood, as well as two splinters from an ibex's vertebrae. Two days after the work started, a heavy snowfall put an end to the investigations and for a month the site was covered in a seven-metre-thick layer of snow.

Grass matting before conservation and restoration

REMAINS

One of the knotted strings discovered during the first archaeological search.

Restored remains of a string knot

SURVEYING WORK

Detailed drawings of the site are an essential element in any excavation work. After taking measurements of the site and its finds, photos are taken and written notes and scale drawings drawn up. The exact location of each find is pinpointed on the site plan. During the second excavation, this work came up against enormous difficulties as snowmelt from higher snowfields flowed constantly into the hollow.

NO HEAVY MACHINERY!

Before undertaking the archaeological investigation of the site, a two-metre-thick layer of snow had to be removed – it took three weeks to move around 600 tons of snow! Diesel-powered machinery could not be used as the exhaust fumes would have distorted the results of ice and sediment tests.

UNUSUAL EXCAVATION TOOLS

For the clearance work some unusual machines were brought in: a steam-blower and dryer. They were used to slowly melt the snow between the rocks and cracks in the stone.

Steam blower

Learning about Life from a Dead Man

Mummies are a window into the past. They reveal what people used to eat, the work they did, how long they lived and the illnesses they suffered. This valuable information can only be obtained with the help of modern scientific methods such as computer tomography and microchemical analysis. Tiny samples of Ötzi's excrement were examined for parasites while elements of Ötzi's DNA could be used for a comparative study of his genetic make-up. Traces of arsenic in his hair indicate that Ötzi was at least passively involved in copper smelting and metalwork. Scientists from all over the world – archaeologists and anthropologists, pathologists and criminologists, microbiologists and botanists, chemists, historians and researchers from numerous other fields – all examined the Iceman over a period of many years.

HOW TALL WAS ÖTZI?

Since Ötzi's left hip was damaged during his recovery and his femur therefore partly exposed, it was possible to measure Ötzi's length and make an estimate of his height. At the time of his death, it was calculated that he measured around 160 centimetres. However today, as a result of the mummification process and the shrinking of the cartilage in his joints and vertebrae, he measures only 153 centimetres. His bones however have maintained their original dimensions.

WORN-OUT HIP JOINT

By means of a digital x-ray of the right hip joint, experts recognised a small fracture between the glenoid cavity and the top of the thighbone – a sign of physical wear and tear.

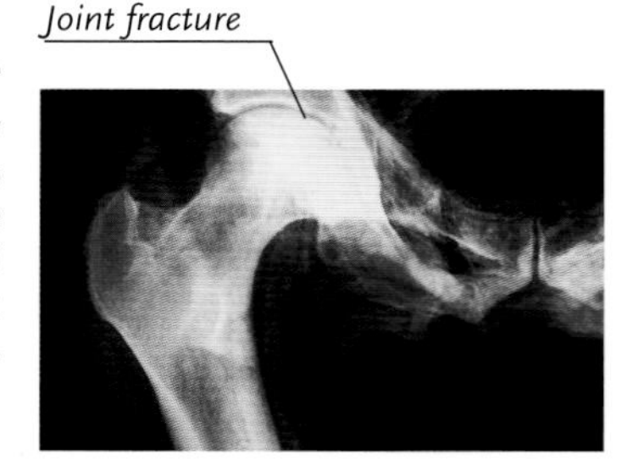

STONE AGE STRESS

From the state of his fingernails, experts concluded that during the last few months of his life, Ötzi was under considerable physical stress. They came to this conclusion on observing three clear beau lines – signs of excessive cell formation caused by stress – on one of his nails. The notches on the end of his nails indicate that Ötzi used them as tools.

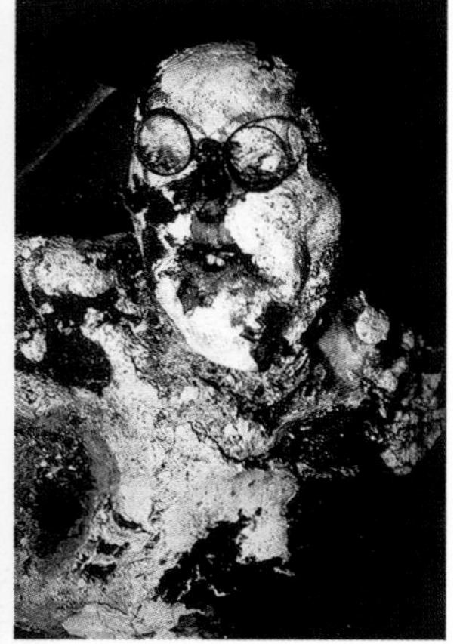

ÖTZI – A SPECIAL CASE AMONG GLACIER DEATHS

Frozen bodies usually bear signs of adipocere. Their body fat is converted to the waxy substance known as adipocere. The body fat dries out leaving the skeleton covered in a sort of armour plating. Adipocere can only develop in a damp environment with limited oxygen. This however was not the case with Ötzi who was mummified under dry airy conditions - covered by a thick blanket of snow.

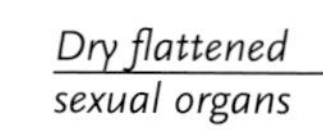

Sections of deer lice - blood-sucking insects - were found in Ötzi's hair.

DENTAL RECORDS

Scientists were able to discover where Ötzi spent his childhood by analysing his tooth enamel. How was this done? They compared the minerals taken from his teeth with soil and water samples from the areas north and south of the main Alpine ridge. During the first months of a person's life, the minerals typical of the landscape where he or she grows up are permanently stored in the teeth.

ABSENCE OF TOOTH DECAY

There is a remarkably wide gap on the upper jaw between the two central incisors.
The fact that Ötzi's teeth show considerable signs of wear is evidence that his diet included stoneground flour which must have contained grit from the milling process. Tooth decay does not appear to have affected Ötzi as his teeth are free of caries.

DIAGNOSIS: BONE FRACTURE

An X-ray of Ötzi's thorax shows numerous bone fractures which must have caused the Iceman a lot of pain. Did he suffer an accident shortly before his death, or were they caused by the pressure of the ice afterwards?

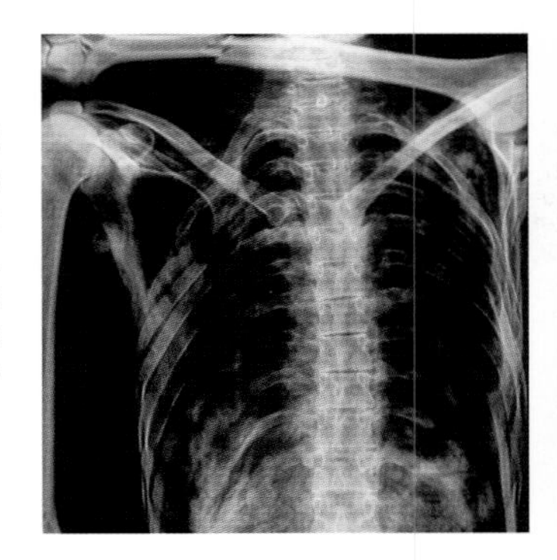

A LOOK INTO HIS LUNGS

Smoke particles had discoloured Ötzi's lungs which confirms that the Iceman used to spend long periods in front of open fires.

HAIRCARE

During the process of mummification, Ötzi's hair completely fell out. Among the numerous locks of hair found among his clothing, there were also samples of human head and body hair. Ötzi had shoulder length, wavy brown hair which was probably not plaited as only single hairs were found. In all probability Ötzi wore a beard to judge by the existence of crinkly hairs, thicker than the rest of his body hair.

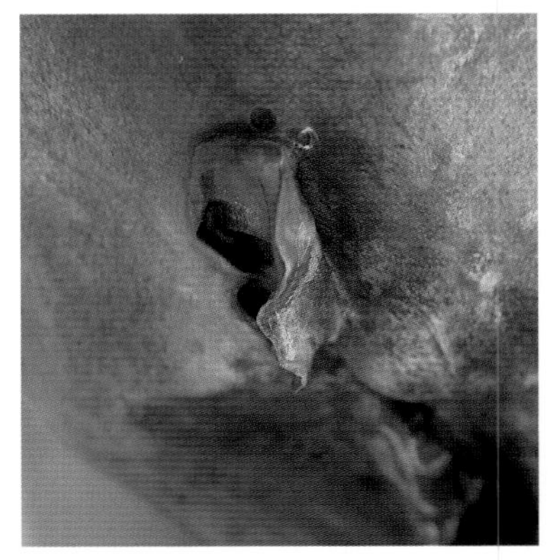

MEMORABLE POSTURE

One of Ötzi's most remarkable features is the unnatural posture of his left arm. His left ear too is folded directly forwards away from its natural position and the fold is noticeably straight. It can therefore be concluded that, after Ötzi died and lay with his clothes frozen to the rock, he must have been slightly moved by the ice.

ALMOST INTACT

Certain information about a person's past can only be obtained when the body tissue is well-preserved. Ötzi's body, apart from the injury to his left hip, is virtually intact and such corpses are far more useful for scientific research than mere bones.

On drying out, the internal organs were severely shrunken

Bald skull

Hip and upper thigh were damaged by the pneumatic drill during the recovery

Flattened thorax

Folded ear

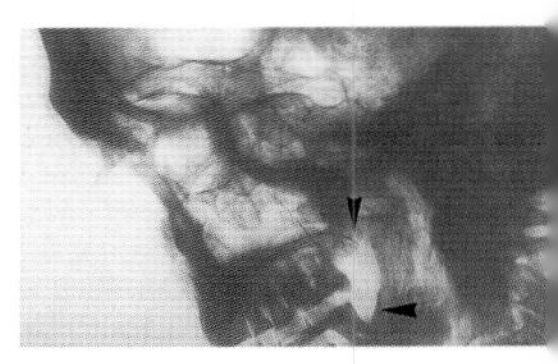

ANATOMICAL ANOMALIES

The scientific examination of the glacier mummy revealed two peculiarities: all four of his wisdom teeth and the twelfth pair of ribs were missing.

Medical Examinations

For the first time in the history of medicine and archaeology, scientists were able to examine a 5,300-year-old mummy using the most advanced diagnostic methods. In order to do so, new technical procedures and instruments were specially developed. A particular challenge to the medical research programme was the endoscopic examination of the mummy. In order to avoid erroneous results, special precision instruments made of titanium were created for carrying out microsurgery. These made it possible to inspect the larynx, the area of the heart and lungs, the aorta, the digestive apparatus and the brain. This journey through the insides of Ötzi's body was captured on film. Visitors to the South Tyrol Museum of Archaeology can see a video of how tiny tissue samples were taken from the Iceman.

ADVANCES IN MODERN MEDICINE

Based on computer tomography data, an Innsbruck radiologist created a three-dimensional model of Ötzi's skull using a procedure called stereo lithography which has long been in use in space exploration and the car industry. A plate is dipped in a bowl containing liquid resin and the CT values are transmitted on to specific points on this plate using a computer-steered laser. At the points touched by the laser-beam, the resin hardens and a layer is formed corresponding to a thin cross-section of the skull. In a short time layer upon layer is built up creating an exact duplicate of the skull. Since Ötzi, stereo lithography has been established as medical technique for the planning and practice of complex brain operations.

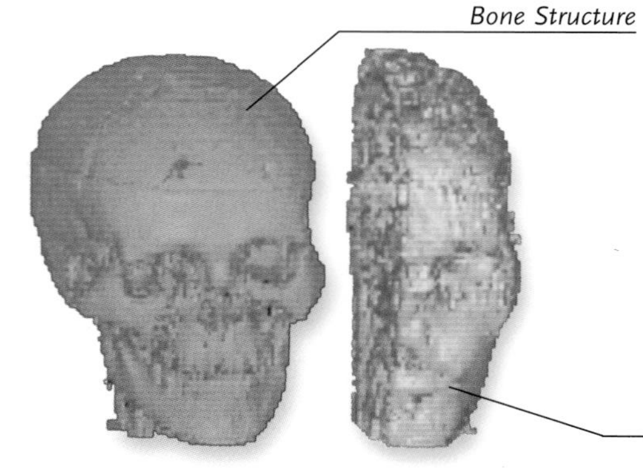

SLIGHTLY OUT OF SHAPE

Ötzi's head was deformed by the pressure of the ice and is in places asymmetrical. For the artificial reconstruction of his face, these deformations were mathematically corrected. Those who have the chance to see the large scale Ötzi reconstruction in the South Tyrol Museum of Archaeology can contemplate his "true", original face.

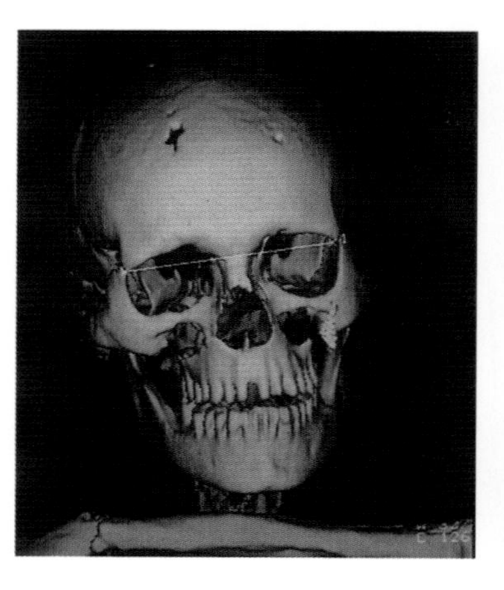

CT TESTING

Since 1977, doctors have been examining mummies using a new technique known as computer tomography (CT). While a normal X-ray only produces two-dimensional images, CT readings can make sectional images taken from a variety of perspectives. Even individual parts of internal organs and tissue can be made visible using CT.

AN INDICATION OF ÖTZI'S AGE

Originally Ötzi was estimated to have been between 25 and 35 years old at the time of his death due to the fact that he has a full set of teeth, with the exception of his wisdom teeth, of course. However the analysis of a thinly sliced bone tissue sample from the upper femur brought more precise results. The normal transformation of bone tissue produces characteristic changes in the bone structure as a person ages. This would make Ötzi around 46 years old.

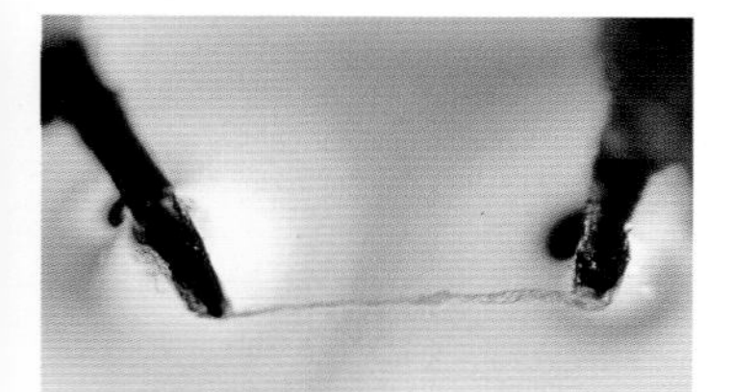

A TRIAL OF STRENGTH

Did any strength remain in Ötzi's muscles? One scientist wanted to find out for sure. He took a muscle fibre from Ötzi's thigh and another from his own leg and stretched them out on a measuring instrument. Ötzi's muscle fibres stretched but did not contract. All the same they were still intact – an astonishing scientific result which nevertheless meant a few painful weeks for the curious scientist!

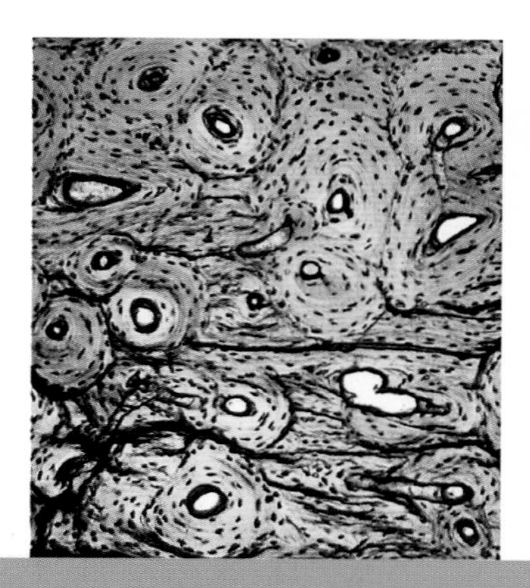

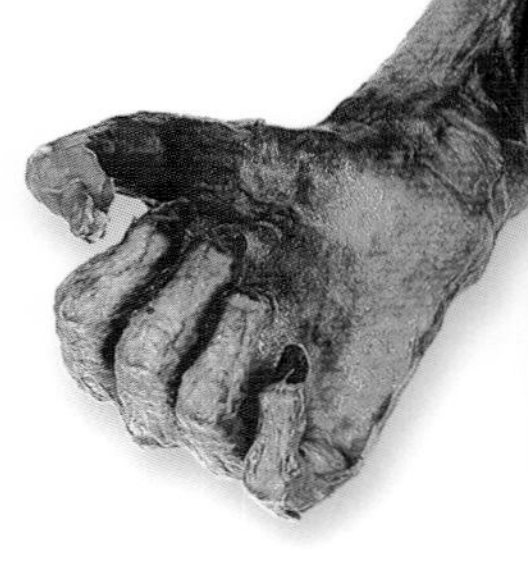

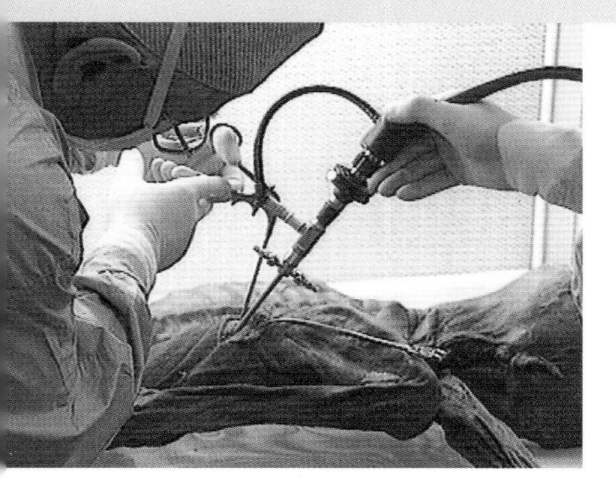

THE ICEMAN'S INNER LIFE

Endoscopes are optical instruments which enable us to see deep inside human bodies without cutting through muscles or bones. They consist of a thin plastic tube with flexible fibre optic clusters. Micro instruments can be attached to the tip of the endoscope in order to perform operations or to take tissue samples. To obtain such samples from Ötzi's internal organs, a small window was cut into his back.

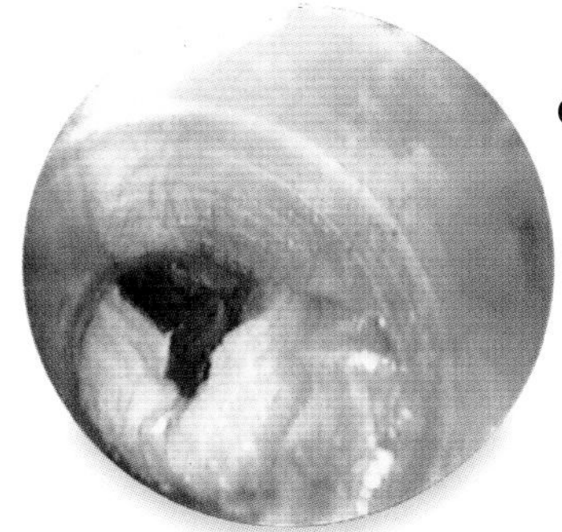

ÖTZI, THE TV STAR

Doctors observed the images recorded by the endoscope from inside Ötzi's body on a TV monitor – in this case a shot of Ötzi's nostrils.

THE MOST CLOSELY EXAMINED PATIENT EVER

From the time the Iceman was discovered in September 1991 until he was taken from Innsbruck to Bolzano in January 1998, a hundred samples were taken from the mummy and examined all over the world. The largest sample weighed 60 mg.

DETAILED DIAGNOSIS

Although Ötzi's internal organs were totally shrunk and shifted position during his long burial, they could be exactly identified by using an endoscope. Here is an image of the glottis in his larynx.

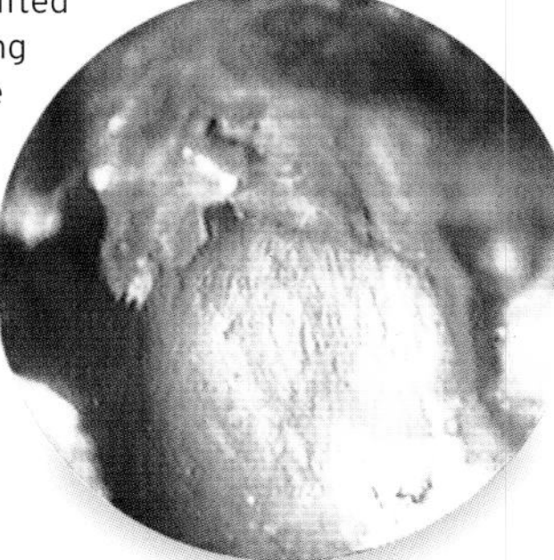

View of the liver

PREHISTORIC PENICILLIN

The birch polypore (Piptoporous betulinus) is a greyish-white fungus that grows principally on older birch trees. In the past folk medicine used it as a drug but its intoxicating effects have not yet been fully established medically. Its value as an antibiotic however has been proven.

MEDICINE

Ötzi carried with him a limited but none the less useful first-aid kit: two spherical pieces of this birch fungus threaded onto leather thongs. These fungi were still used at the beginning of the 20th century to stop bleeding.

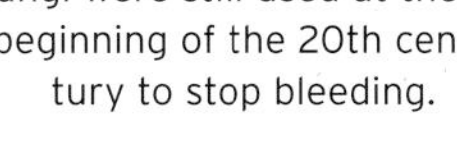

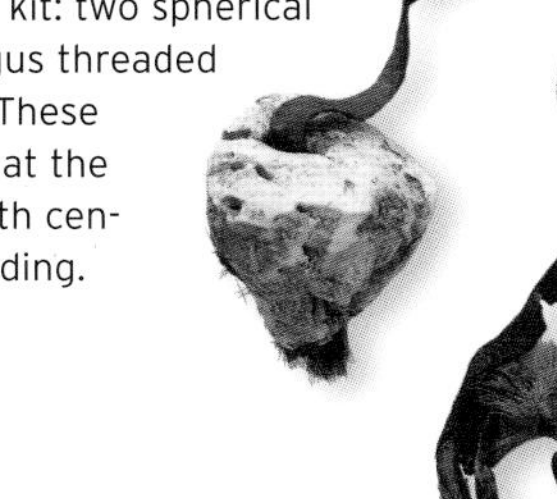

Ötzi's Tattoos

At the moment of the Iceman's discovery, drawings were noticed on his back which were at first taken to be branding. Soon people realised that they were in fact tattoos. Unlike modern tattoos, these were not made using needles but with tiny cuts into which powdered charcoal was rubbed. Around 60 tattoos in the form of groups of lines or crosses were found, located next to his spinal column, on the right knee, on the calves and the ankle joints. These were the places where Ötzi's body, on account of his age and the constant strain he underwent, showed particular signs of wear. He must have suffered considerable pain at these points. By cutting through fine nerves, pain could be alleviated. Ötzi's tattoos therefore probably had a medical function and were not made for decorative reasons.

WORN-OUT

Many of the tattoos are on his ankle joints. When doctors examined these joints, the X-rays displayed signs of advanced sclerosis (a pathological hardening of the arteries) as well as a narrowing of the interarticular space.

STONE AGE THERAPY

Ötzi was not in good health at the time of his death. His spine, ankle, hip and knee joints were strained, his teeth worn down, his aorta hardened and his nasal bone broken. He also had parasitic worms and a cyst on his spinal cord. All these problems give the impression that Ötzi's tattoos - the oldest ever seen on a human body - were an early form of medical treatment.

ASTONISHING PARALLELS

This nomad prince of Pazyryk in the Siberian Altai mountains lived around 400 BC. Besides the magnificent decorative tattoos on his shoulders and arms, he also displays signs of medically motivated designs on both the left and right-hand side of his spinal column. The location of these tattoos correspond exactly to those of the Iceman.

VITAMIN PILLS

Not only did Ötzi use medicine for the treatment of illness but also in a preventative manner through the discovery of therapeutic substances. Evidence for this lies in the sloeberry which was found beside him. Due to its high vitamin and mineral content, this fruit has long been cherished.

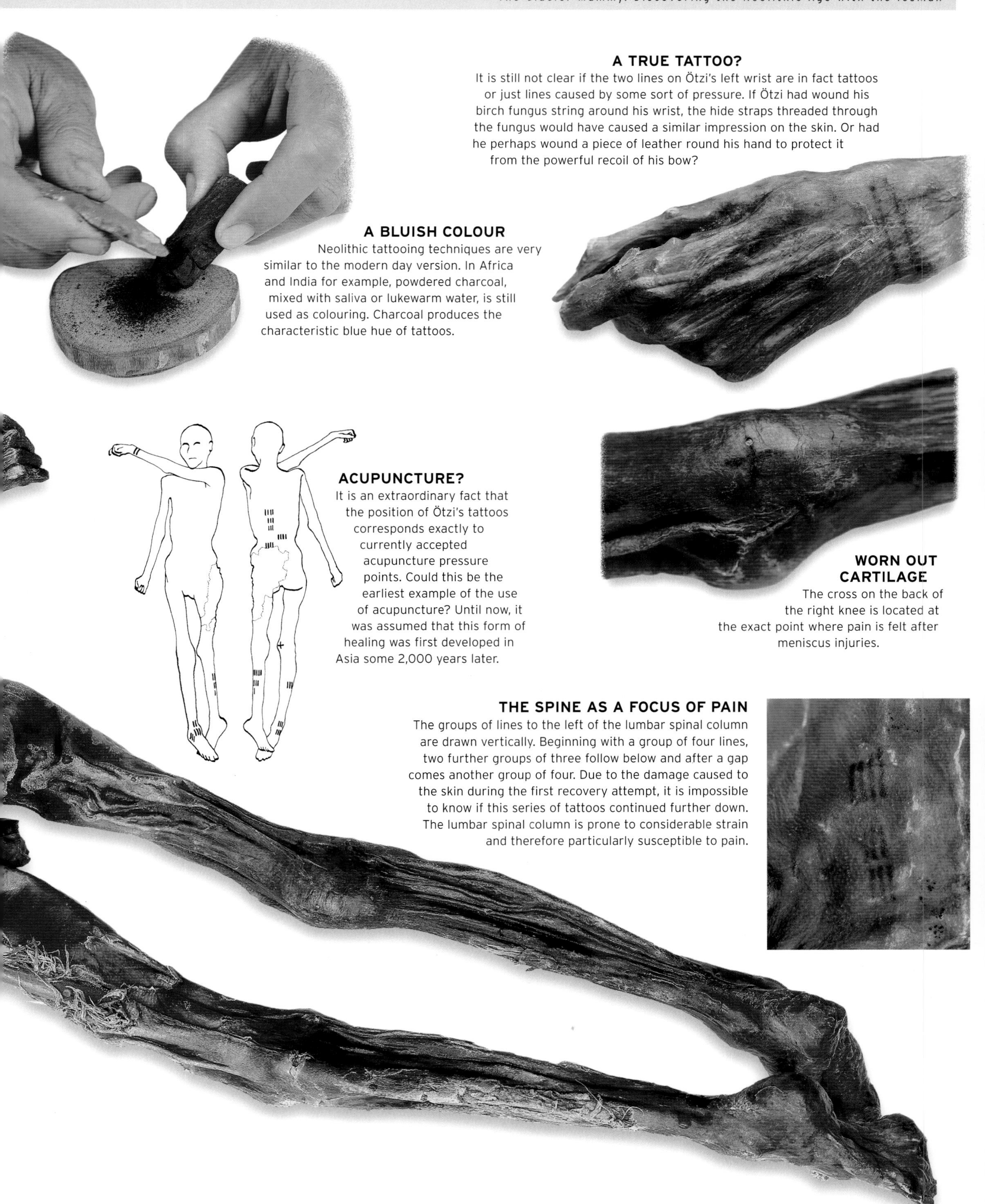

A TRUE TATTOO?

It is still not clear if the two lines on Ötzi's left wrist are in fact tattoos or just lines caused by some sort of pressure. If Ötzi had wound his birch fungus string around his wrist, the hide straps threaded through the fungus would have caused a similar impression on the skin. Or had he perhaps wound a piece of leather round his hand to protect it from the powerful recoil of his bow?

A BLUISH COLOUR

Neolithic tattooing techniques are very similar to the modern day version. In Africa and India for example, powdered charcoal, mixed with saliva or lukewarm water, is still used as colouring. Charcoal produces the characteristic blue hue of tattoos.

ACUPUNCTURE?

It is an extraordinary fact that the position of Ötzi's tattoos corresponds exactly to currently accepted acupuncture pressure points. Could this be the earliest example of the use of acupuncture? Until now, it was assumed that this form of healing was first developed in Asia some 2,000 years later.

WORN OUT CARTILAGE

The cross on the back of the right knee is located at the exact point where pain is felt after meniscus injuries.

THE SPINE AS A FOCUS OF PAIN

The groups of lines to the left of the lumbar spinal column are drawn vertically. Beginning with a group of four lines, two further groups of three follow below and after a gap comes another group of four. Due to the damage caused to the skin during the first recovery attempt, it is impossible to know if this series of tattoos continued further down. The lumbar spinal column is prone to considerable strain and therefore particularly susceptible to pain.

Mountain Gear

The Iceman was perfectly equipped for high mountain terrain. A knee-length hide coat protected him from the wind and cold and his leggings gave him considerable freedom of movement. For the rain and snow, Ötzi wore elaborately woven grass matting over his shoulders which helped moisture to run off and protected the leather garments he wore beneath. His shoes were also intricately constructed and ideal for long treks over rough terrain or sharp glacier ice. To keep out the cold, Ötzi stuffed his shoes with hay and over them wore robust deerskin outer shoes whose bearskin soles even had some tread. A comparison of Neolithic and modern day mountain gear shows that although the equipment has changed considerably, Ötzi's kit was nonetheless highly effective.

ESSENTIAL HEADGEAR
Humans lose a lot of body heat through the head so up in the cold windy mountains good headgear is particularly important. Ötzi kept his bearskin cap in place by tightening the leather chin straps.

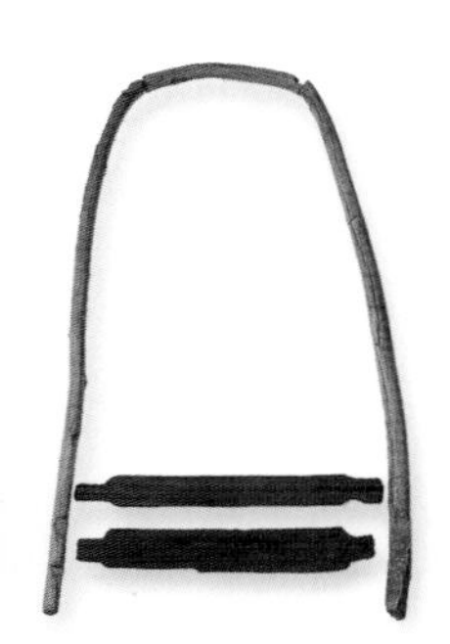

CARRYING HIS LOAD
Comparable back-packs are still used today in the Alps for transporting loads. Ötzi's backpack bears a strong resemblance to the light metal frames used on modern rucksacks.

A SMALL FIRST-AID KIT
Ötzi's few yet extremely effective medicines were the two fungus balls – pieces of birch polypore – particularly useful as disinfectants and stypics.

TINDER
Fungal tinder was an essential element in Neolithic fire-making. This easy-to-light tree fungus had to be kept dry at all costs. Ötzi carried his in a leather belt pouch.

READY FOR ACTION
As Ötzi always needed his small flint knife for cutting, carving or skinning hunted prey, he attached it to his belt.

EMBER CONTAINER
Ötzi carried burning embers in this birch-bark container in order to be able to make a fire as quickly as possible. In this way, he was not forced to start from scratch whenever damp weather made the tinder difficult to light.

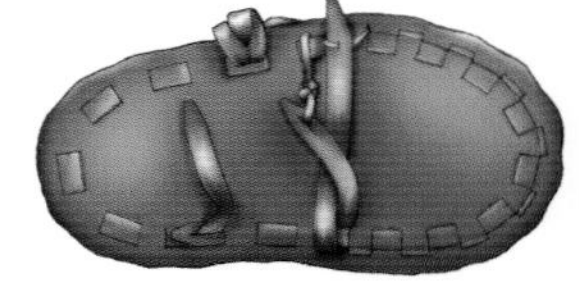

SLIP-PROOF
Ötzi's shoe soles had criss-cross leather straps, giving them a measure of tread.

NO POTTERY
A light flexible birch-bark container was much easier for Ötzi to transport than heavy breakable clay pots, the usual receptacles of his time. The inner side of Ötzi's other receptacle was not blackened by soot but retains its natural yellow-white colour, suggesting that he used it for carrying food.

PRACTICAL
Before Ötzi's discovery, it was not known that footwear consisting of an inner and outer shoe had then been developed.

TRIED AND TESTED MATERIALS

Mountain climbers prefer their headgear and ear protection to be made of natural absorbent materials due to the considerable warmth and perspiration given off through the head. When it rains or snows, the anorak hood can be pulled over the woolly hat.

THERMOS FLASK AND LUNCH BOX

As Ötzi's possessions included nothing resembling a drinking flask, we do not know if he was carrying liquids with him. A birch-bark container would have served perfectly as a container for solid food, being as light as modern day tin provision boxes.

MODERN MOUNTAINEERING EQUIPMENT

The use of leather and hide for mountaineering garments has long been in disuse. In the Alps, leather knickerbockers continued to be worn up until a few decades ago. Wool and cotton have also been replaced by lighter, more breathable artificial fibres such as fleece. The function of Ötzi's grass cape has been taken over by coated waterproof materials. However, unlike natural materials, these are not recyclable.

Fleece jacket

FIRE ON DEMAND

Matches are still part of a mountaineer's kit but they remain just as unreliable in wet weather as Ötzi's true-tinder fungus.

FIRST-AID KIT

The contents of a modern mountaineering first-aid kit include stypics, plasters and bandages for treating wounds, medicines to improve blood circulation, painkillers and sun protection.

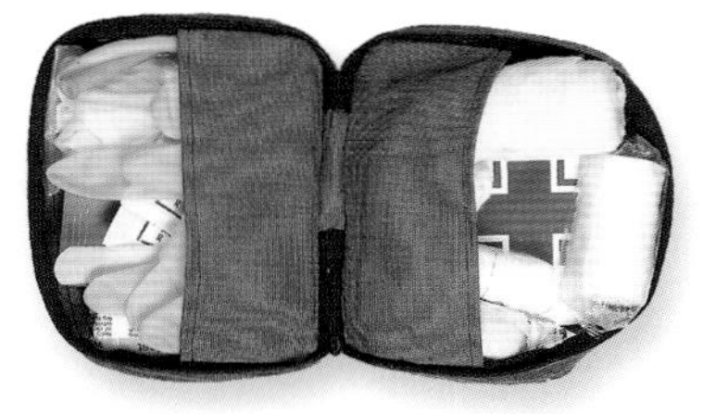

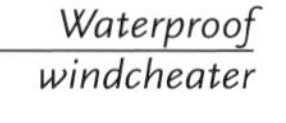

Waterproof windcheater

INNER AND OUTER SHOES

Ötzi's footwear was built in much the same way as modern walking boots. A soft insulated inner section and a stiffer, more waterproof outer layer. Today the inner shoe is generally made of artificial fibres and the outer shoe of leather or plastic.

STILL ESSENTIAL

The pocket knife – ready for use just like in Ötzi's time. The blade still has to be stored safely but no longer by means of a mini-masterpiece of weaving. Today a closing mechanism or a leather sheath is the usual protection.

Backpack

SLIP-PROOF SNOWSHOES

The type of snow shoe still in use today is constructed on the same principle as the leather straps which criss-crossed the soles of Ötzi's shoes. They have the same effect as the tread on a deeply notched sole.

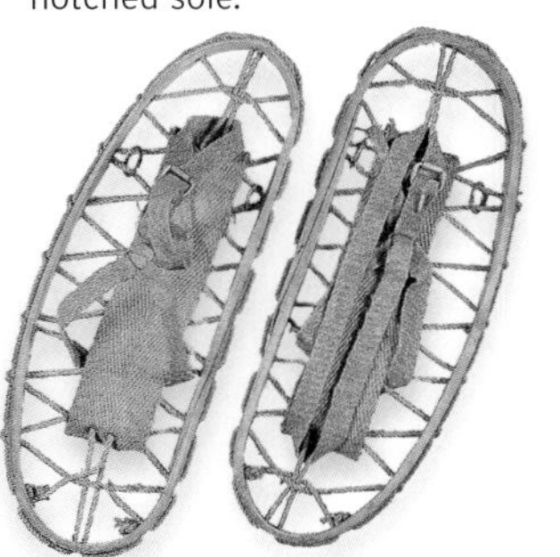

Layered artificial fabric trousers

GROOVED AND TUFTED

The soles of walking shoes have to hold firm on scree and snow and for this reason have a very deep tread. Although Ötzi's shoes were made of leather, they were not smooth. The inner side of bearskin has a very effective nobbly surface.

Ice boots

Leather and Hide for Clothing

Before the Iceman was discovered, we had only the vaguest idea of what people in Neolithic times used to wear. Organic material rarely survives for long and only under very specific conditions. The exceptional find on the Hauslabjoch confirms that, for winter clothing at least, leather was the dominant material. Although Ötzi did not wear any woven materials, the accurate cutting, careful sewing and absolute suitability of Ötzi's garments suggest that our ancestors were highly cultivated people. The variety of colours on the strips that made up Ötzi's hide coat also indicate a certain degree of fashion consciousness on his part.

OVERCOAT OR PONCHO?
Ötzi wore a knee-length upper garment made of goat hide. It is no longer possible to say whether it had any form of fastening and there is no trace of sleeves. Very possibly this hide garment never had sleeves and may well have been a poncho rather than an overcoat.

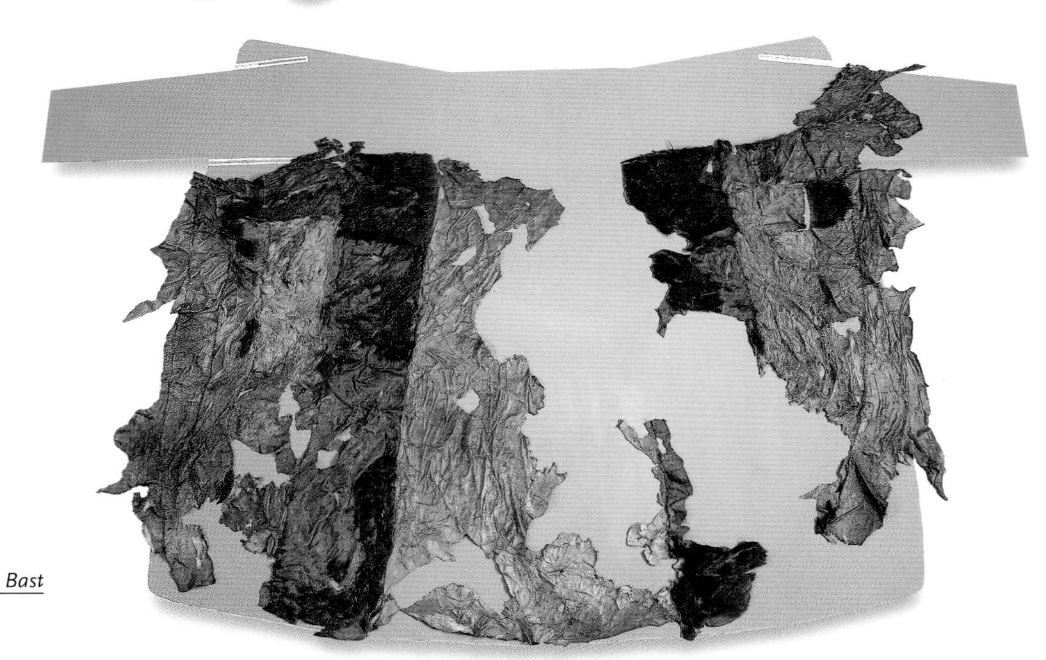

ÖTZI'S STRIPEY LOOK
The individual pieces of hide from Ötzi's upper garment were sewn together so as to create a pattern of light and dark strips. The remains of his coat, along with all his other possessions, are on display at the South Tyrol Museum of Archaeology in Bolzano and give a vivid impression of how this item of clothing looked.

AN EYE FOR DETAIL
The coat was carefully sewn together from square pieces of hide using overlock stitching.

Bast

FINE THREAD
Finely twisted animal sinews as well as grass and tree bast were used as thread.

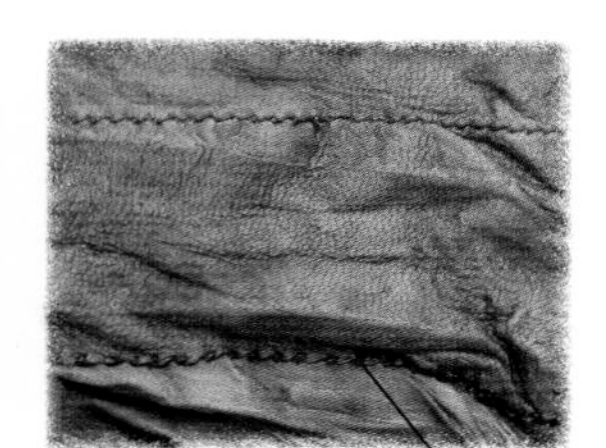

MENDED
Two people may have well sewn Ötzi's hide coat. One used animal sinews for extremely accurate stitching while the other performed rudimentary repairs using grass stems.

ECO-UNDERWEAR
Only the front part of Ötzi's soft, thin goatskin loin cloth has been preserved. As with all Ötzi's clothing, the rear part was the first to see daylight and so disintegrated due to the effects of bright sunshine and strong winds.

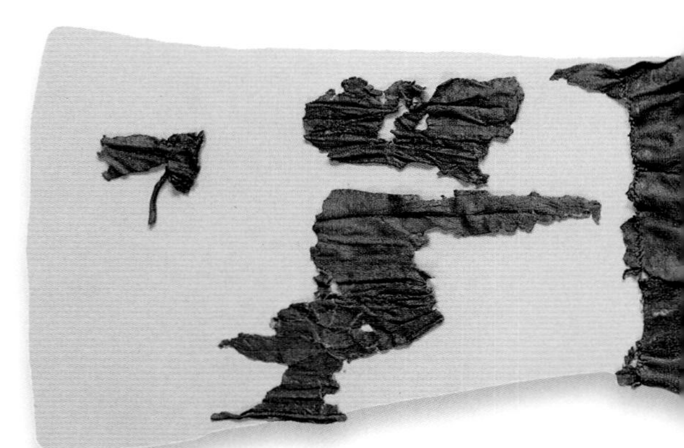

LONGISH FLAPS
Deerskin flaps were sewn on to the bottom end of his leggings. These were tucked into Ötzi's shoes and knotted to the upper structure.

STRETCHING, SCRAPING AND HAIR REMOVAL
The first stage in the production of leather is the stretching of the hide on a frame to avoid creasing. The inner side would be cleaned of fat and remains of tissue with a flint blade to make it more supple. The outer side was doused with water or urine so that the fur would fall out.

GOATSKIN
Most of Ötzi's clothes were made of goatskin. Sheep and goats were the first animals to be domesticated by man. Although cattle, as providers of meat and milk products as well as sinews and hides, are more valuable, the stock of sheep and goats was far greater. In the harsh mountain terrain they were much easier to keep and could survive the harsh winters without difficulty.

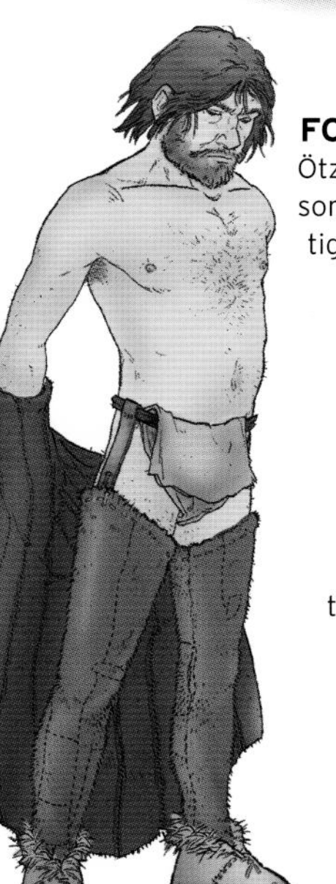

FOOT FREE
Ötzi's leggings looked something like leather tights without the feet.

LIKE AN AMERICAN INDIAN
Ötzi's leggings were made of goatskin and bear a strong resemblance to those of the North American Indians, some of whom lived in identical climatic conditions to the Iceman.

STRAPS
At the top of his leggings two broad hide straps were sewn on. The tops of the straps were split into two ends, enabling Ötzi to tie his leggings to his belt.

SHOELACES
The uppers of Ötzi's shoes were made of deerskin. They could be fastened with leather laces and attached to the flaps on his leggings.

Knotted and Plaited

The Iceman's clothing primarily consists of tanned hides. Only three of his possessions were plaited or knotted – the grass-netted structure of his shoes, the long plaited grass matting and the sheath made of strips of bast for his flint dagger. Surprisingly, woven items are entirely absent from Ötzi's clothes and equipment. Until the discovery of the mummy, it was widely believed that the art of weaving had already reached an advanced level in the Neolithic age, with people generally using clothes made of woven material. Existing archaeological knowledge of textiles has had to be seriously reappraised and corrected.

LIKE A THATCHED ROOF

Grass and straw matting is extremely waterproof. The horizontal knotting on Ötzi's grass matting is placed as far apart as possible to keep the rainwater out.

MULTIFUNCTIONAL

The woven grass matting was originally taken to be a sleeveless cape that Ötzi could easily throw over himself or remove at will. It was thought that, for someone who spent so long in the open air, such a garment had numerous advantages: protection during bad weather, camouflage when hunting, insulation from the damp ground and a blanket on cold nights. Doubts have since emerged. If Ötzi had really worn the matting as a cape, it would have been wider at the shoulders, which is not the case however.

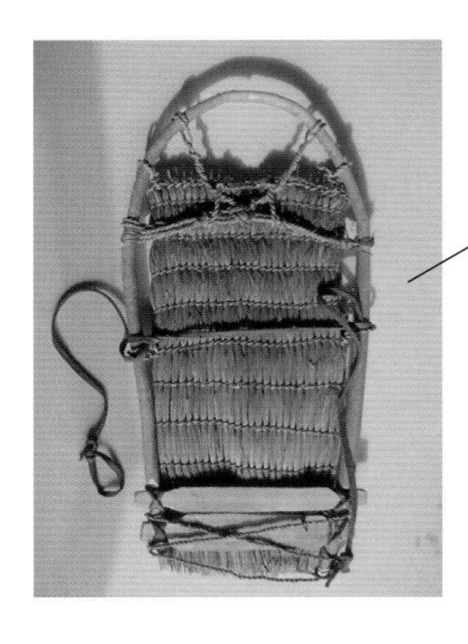

The backpack reconstructed

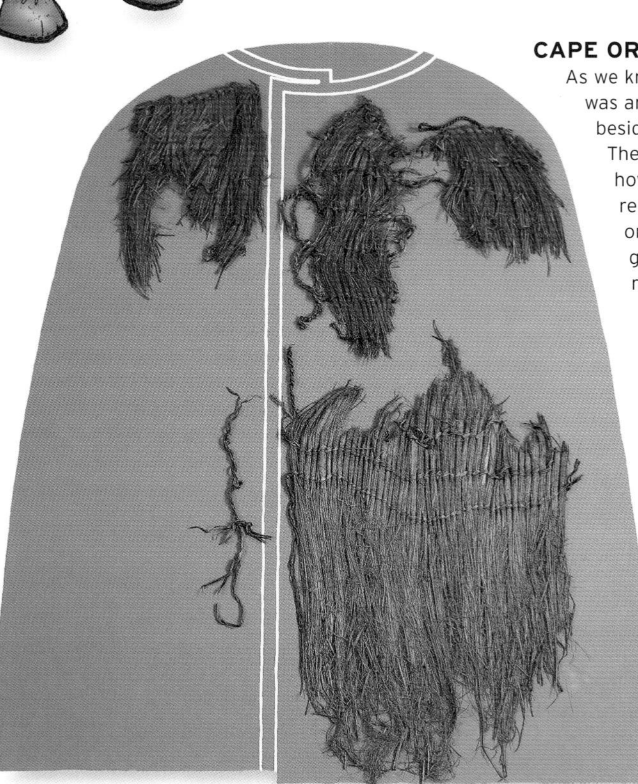

CAPE OR BACKPACK?

As we know, the frame of a backpack was among the objects that lay beside the glacier mummy. The bag section or container however was never found, but remains of string were visible on the frame. Could Ötzi's grass matting really be the missing bag?

REEDLIKE

The cape was plaited out of one metre long Alpine reed sweetgrass. For the elaboration of such capes and mats today, marsh reeds are generally used.

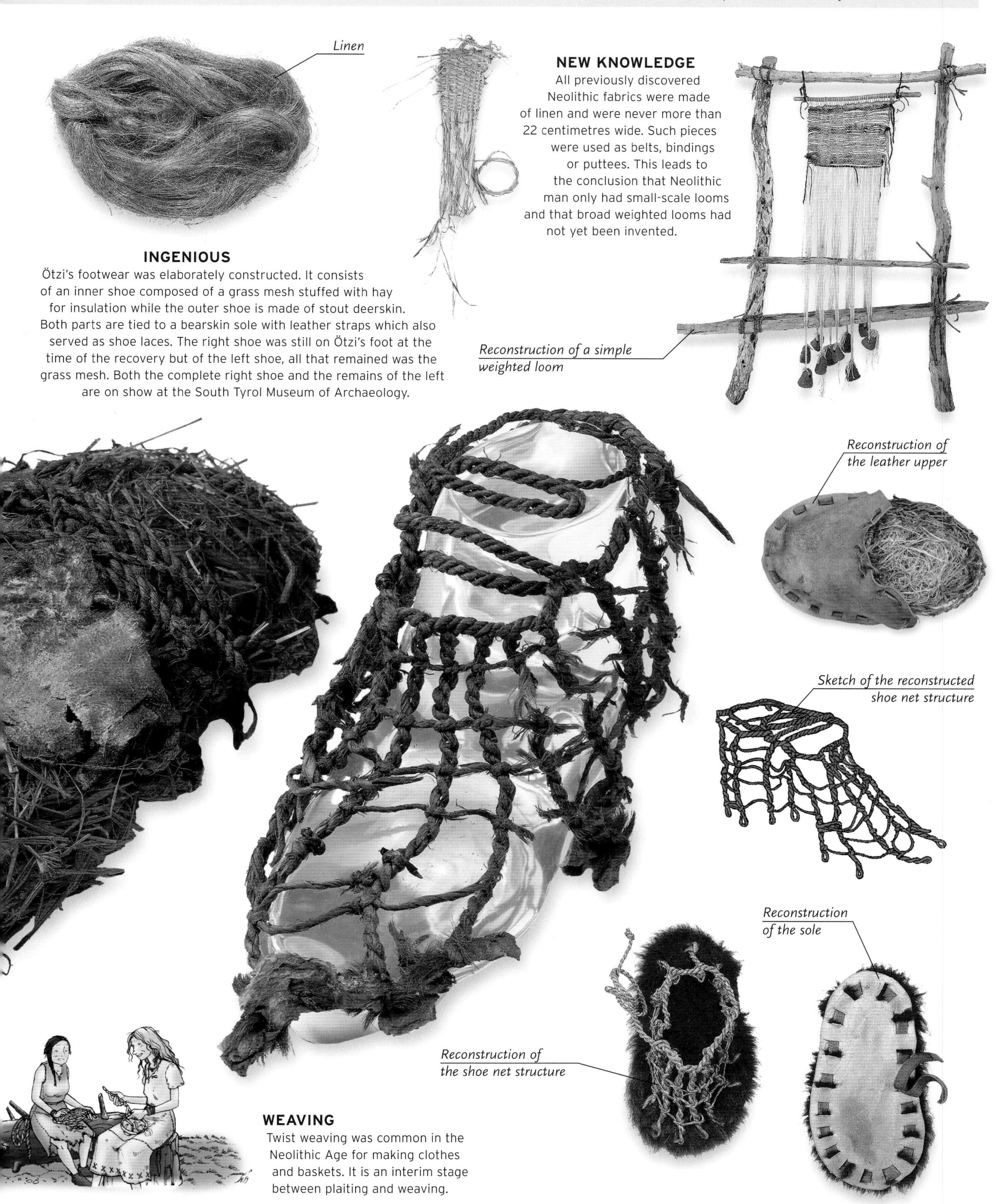

NEW KNOWLEDGE

All previously discovered Neolithic fabrics were made of linen and were never more than 22 centimetres wide. Such pieces were used as belts, bindings or puttees. This leads to the conclusion that Neolithic man only had small-scale looms and that broad weighted looms had not yet been invented.

INGENIOUS

Ötzi's footwear was elaborately constructed. It consists of an inner shoe composed of a grass mesh stuffed with hay for insulation while the outer shoe is made of stout deerskin. Both parts are tied to a bearskin sole with leather straps which also served as shoe laces. The right shoe was still on Ötzi's foot at the time of the recovery but of the left shoe, all that remained was the grass mesh. Both the complete right shoe and the remains of the left are on show at the South Tyrol Museum of Archaeology.

WEAVING

Twist weaving was common in the Neolithic Age for making clothes and baskets. It is an interim stage between plaiting and weaving.

The Belt Pouch

In order to survive in his surroundings, Ötzi had to be extremely well-prepared. Everything he needed to start a fire or make weapons had to be carried on his person. Some of these useful objects were very valuable and their loss, or dampening in the case of his fungus tinder, could have been tragic. What better to carry such objects than a belt pouch? Ötzi wore a belt around his waist with a sewn-on pouch which contained valuables such as pieces of fungus tinder, a bone awl and three flint tools – a scraper, a drill and a sharp flint flake. Today ramblers, cyclists and travellers in general still use belt pouches similar to Ötzi's old belt. Sewn-in pockets on the inner side of belts are also common for protecting valuables and are similar to medieval money bags.

A CURIOUS CLUSTER

At first taken to be birch tar, this black knobbly mass found in the pouch was later identified by botanists as a piece of fungus tinder mixed with tiny particles of iron pyrites. This tree fungus constitutes a prehistoric firelighter.

Leather closing strip

Grass string

ALWAYS AT THE READY

The frayed grass string on the handle of the flint dagger corresponds directly to the remains of a knot on the belt. We can safely conclude that Ötzi hung his dagger and sheath from his belt, to the right of the pouch.

Grass string

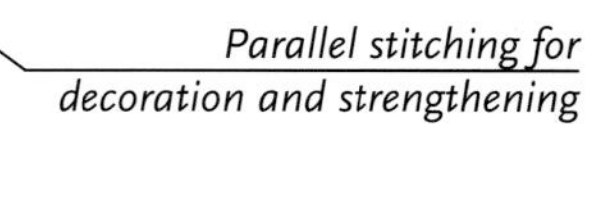

PINPOINTING MATERIALS

Ötzi's belt pouch is made of calf hide. Since the progenitor of our domestic cattle, the aurochs, died out in 1627, it cannot be ascertained if the hide came from a domestic or a wild animal.

Domestic cow

NO BUTTONS

We do not know how Ötzi fastened his hide coat but he may have used his belt for this purpose.

WELL-WORN

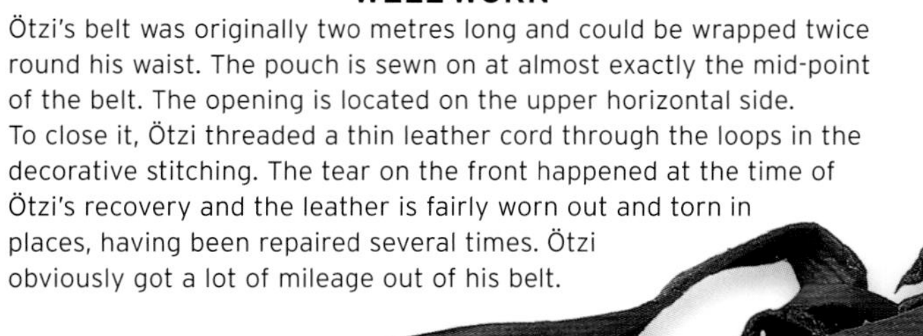

Ötzi's belt was originally two metres long and could be wrapped twice round his waist. The pouch is sewn on at almost exactly the mid-point of the belt. The opening is located on the upper horizontal side. To close it, Ötzi threaded a thin leather cord through the loops in the decorative stitching. The tear on the front happened at the time of Ötzi's recovery and the leather is fairly worn out and torn in places, having been repaired several times. Ötzi obviously got a lot of mileage out of his belt.

Opening

Rip

The retoucheur hung from here

Decorative stitching

MULTI-USE

Ötzi used this flint tool for scraping, scratching, carving, planing or smoothing. On one edge there are signs of so-called sickle gloss. This is formed when silicic acid-rich plant stems are cut and so it must have been used in the making of Ötzi's grass cape.

FLINT DRILLS

Did Ötzi use this flint tool to pierce holes in his quiver and attach a supporting rod?

CONVENIENCE FIRE

Ötzi had two ways of making fire – either with the flint firelighter he kept in his belt pouch or with the embers he carried in the birch-bark container. Using the latter was far easier and the flint must have been there only as a back-up.

NEEDLE SHARP POINT

This tool was made out of the foot bone of an animal and was probably damaged during the Iceman's recovery. Ötzi may have used it to make small holes in leather or for tattooing.

RAZOR SHARP

Ötzi used this flint blade for fine carving and cutting. At the top, minute particles of feathers were discovered with the help of a microscope specially constructed at the University of Canberra in Australia. This proves that Ötzi used this blade to prepare feathers as flights for his arrows.

FASTENED TO THE BELT

To the left of the pouch, Ötzi fastened one of his most important tools, the retoucheur. The leather on the left hand side of the pouch shows signs of wear as if the retoucheur may have been attached to it with a string.

Notch for attaching a string

The Flint Dagger and Retoucheur

Finely crafted flint daggers like Ötzi's correspond to the technical standards of 5,000 years ago. The Iceman used the dagger to work his bow and, as microscopic blood samples show, slaughter domestic and hunted animals. Also at hand was another small inconspicuous tool – the retoucheur. Just like the dagger, there is a notch cut into the handle, probably so that Ötzi could attach the retoucheur to his belt. This pencil-like tool with a dark lump at the end gave experts no end of headaches. At first they had no idea as to the object's possible use and for some time thought it to be a fire-lighting tool.

LIKE A PENCIL
When the working end of the retoucheur was blunt or worn out, it could be sharpened like a pencil.

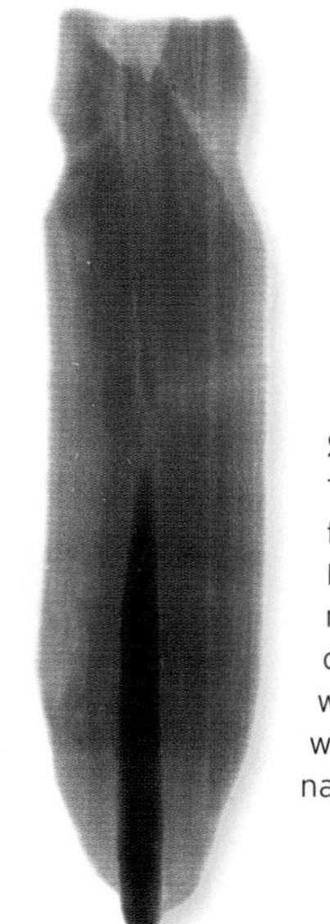

STUCK WELL IN
The X-ray shows that the protruding point was part of a longer stag antler spike which reached right into the middle of the wooden shaft. As this was impossible to remove, it was difficult to ascertain the nature of the material.

Notch

ELASTIC ENOUGH
The shaft of the retoucheur is made of a piece of lime wood with the bark removed. Lime wood is soft yet hard-wearing and easily crafted.

Awl point

A PRECISION TOOL
Ötzi produced flint blades with the retoucheur by stamping out their shape and then sharpening (or retouching) them. The tool is almost twelve centimetres long with the point protruding about four millimetres.

HARDENED FOR SPECIAL USES
The carefully carved and polished spike inside the retoucheur is a piece of stag's antler. Ötzi hardened the end with fire giving it a sooty black appearance.

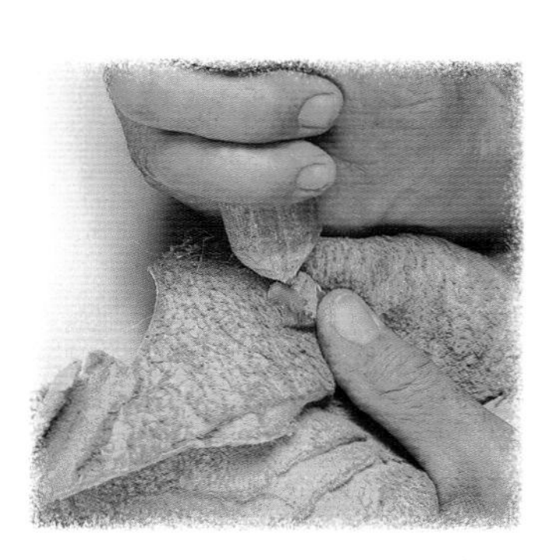

RETOUCHING
Using the hardened point of the tool, fine shell-shaped splinters from an unworked flint were hammered off. In this way the desired form of the blade or arrowhead could be elaborated or a cutting edge sharpened.

A LITTLE WORK OF ART

The dagger sheath is a fine example of careful plaiting. Unfortunately, it was also damaged by the drill during the recovery work. No other comparable prehistoric artefact had ever been found before.

ASTONISHINGLY SMALL

Ötzi's dagger measured only 12.8 centimetres. If the blade had been found without the handle, it would have probably been taken for an arrowhead. The blade point was already broken during Ötzi's lifetime. As the blade was driven so far into the handle, it slightly split the long-grained wood and so was tightly bound with a thin animal sinew. Twisted animal sinews are as tough as nylon and were the strongest material available to Ötzi. The grass string wound round the handle notch is torn and now only six centimetres long. Just as today we carry pocket knives on a small chain, Ötzi must have fastened his dagger to the belt pouch with this string.

CHOICE RAW MATERIALS

The dagger handle is made of ash (Fraxinus excelsior). This wood is flexible, with long fine fibres. It is still put to many uses such as the crafting of wooden bowls, tool handles and shafts.

FLINT MINING IN THE SOUTHERN ALPS

For months a mineralogist searched the limestone areas of the Northern and Southern Alps for flint bearing strata until he discovered the quarry where the flint for Ötzi's tools originated – the Monti Lessini, east of Lake Garda, Italy.

ANCIENT TECHNIQUES – MODERN MATERIALS

It took Ötzi about 15 minutes to sharpen the blade of his dagger. In an equally short space of time, Australian aborigines produce arrowheads out of modern materials such as glass.

RETOUCHING ON BOTH SIDES

Both sides of the blade of Ötzi's dagger were retouched. This technique was also used on his axe blade and is known as double-edge retouching.

Experimental Archaeology

When archaeologists uncover artefacts whose meaning and function is unknown to them, they try to decipher these secrets by, among other things, comparing them anthropologically by creating ethnographic analogies. They compare objects belonging to present day primitive peoples who live on a similar cultural level to those being investigated, asking representatives of these people what these objects are used for. If this is not successful, experimental archaeology is the next step. Objects are manufactured using the same materials and are tested to see how they can best be used. This was the case with Ötzi's retoucheur. Up until then, identical or similar objects had not been found. The first attempts at experimental archaeology confirmed that this puzzling tool was used for the preparation of flint blades.

Three blades sharpened with the retoucheur

A SUCCESSFUL EXPERIMENT

In order to sharpen this flintstone, an American archaeologist copied Ötzi's retoucheur and in a short space of time created an absolutely effective tool.

AN IMPORTANT DISCOVERY

Ötzi's retoucheur had a split along the shaft. An archaeologist cut a similar split into a retoucheur he made himself and discovered that the pressure of the hard antler inside the soft lime wood made the former fray. Only then could the retoucheur work properly.

SOLID LAVA

Apart from flint, man has made use of other types of rock. Obsidian was also treasured by many cultures around the world as a raw material for elaborating tools and jewellery. Obsidian is a vitreous volcanic rock produced by the rapid cooling of lava. As with flint, sharp edges can be fashioned.

Unworked flint blade

UNDER PRESSURE

The really detailed work was done by removing splinters with the pressure of the retoucheur. This is the only way to sharpen the sides into fine blades.

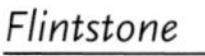

Flintstone

AN IDEAL RAW MATERIAL

Flint is relatively common and breaks into shell-like pieces whose edges can be sharpened. This is why it was used in the Stone Age for making sharp tools. Over the thousands of years that followed, early man perfected his craft techniques to produce virtually any type of tool out of flint.

Flint shard

BLOW BY BLOW

First of all, an unworked stone would be broken into blades and chips using a so-called hammerstone.

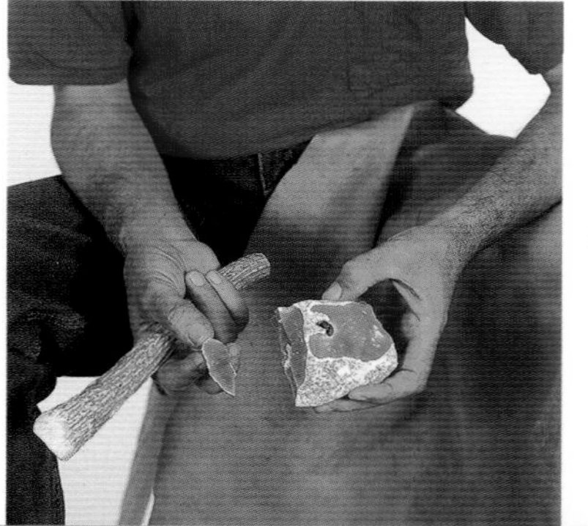

A VARIETY OF TOOLS

Hammer blows can be cushioned by using a piece of hardwood, a bone, an antler or a wooden hammer between the hammerstone and the flint.

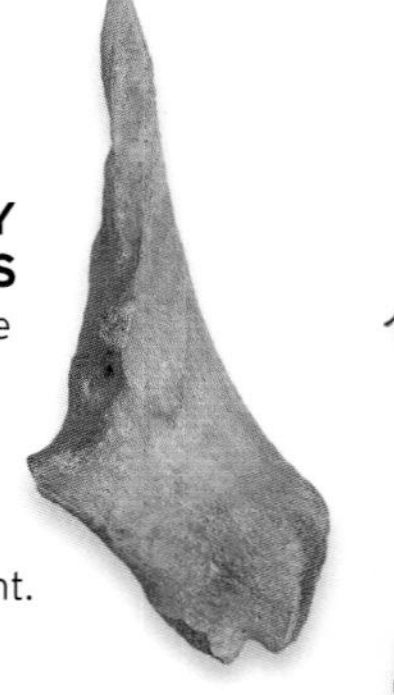

PUTTING IT TO THE TEST

Archaeologists experiment with flint to check their hypotheses on Neolithic working techniques and materials. In this way they are able to discover the uses of previously unknown tools. Other experiments include the planting of ancient varieties of wheat to obtain information about yields, susceptibility to disease, dependence on weather conditions and nutritional value.

SHARP AND ROUND

A small blade like the copy shown here was used by Ötzi to halve feather quills for arrow flights. He carried this small tool in his belt pouch.

NO SCISSORS REQUIRED

Experiments using a razor-sharp flint blade show that leather or knotted grass can be cut without applying any great pressure.

LONG LAMELLA

The art of preparing flints consists of knowing how the stone will break. For example long lamellas can be beaten out using a cushioning object such as an antler between the hammerstone and the flint and are ideal as raw blades. Round sharp flints are more appropriate for cutting and carving.

The Copper Axe

Ötzi's 60cm-long copper axe is the world's first totally preserved prehistoric axe. The blade is embedded in a forked shaft. Until a few centuries before Christ, axe hafts were cut from suitably mature wood. The Celts inserted their iron axes into forked shafts, a technique probably borrowed from their Southern neighbours, the Greeks and the Romans. Among other things, the characteristic shape of Ötzi's axe was an important clue as to the Iceman's age. Other conclusions could be drawn from the blade. As copper is a soft metal, some scientists doubted the suitability of Ötzi's axe as a tool or a weapon. An experiment using a reproduction of the axe brought conclusive proof: a 50-year-old yew was felled in less than 45 minutes.

HIDDEN

The forked shaft is just seven centimetres long and is almost completely hidden under the shaft binding. The axe blade fits exactly into the shaft with only 2.6 centimetres protruding. The binding was completed with a coat of birch tar.

Axe blade

Shaft binding

Malachite

SMELTING

Early metalworkers used bellows and blowpipes to reach the temperatures necessary to smelt copper. Copper smelting originated in the Near East over 8,000 years ago, spreading to Central Europe via Hungary before establishing itself in the Alps during Ötzi's lifetime.

SPLENDID COLOURS

The raw material for Ötzi's axe was not obtained from below ground. Copper ore such as green malachite lies in thin layers on the surface of many copper deposits and it is easy to scrape off and collect.

Copper smelting furnace in the South Tyrol Museum of Archeology

HOW IS COPPER OBTAINED FROM THE ORE?

Layers of chipped and sulphur calcinated copper ore were placed in layers with charcoal in a walled furnace. Oxygen was supplied by means of bellows. After several hours, the temperature reaches 1,100°C making the copper separate from the iron bearing clinkers which flow out of a breach in the oven. The molten copper remains on the furnace floor.

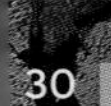

A FURTHER PECULIARITY

Ötzi's axe is the first to be found with a yew haft. Similar finds are normally made of ash. The wood of the yew (Taxus baccata) has a number of excellent qualities – resin-free, highly flexible, long-lasting, tough and heavy – but, due to its very hardness, it is difficult to fashion.

THE RIGHT-ANGLED SHAFT

Ötzi made his most valuable tool out of a piece of the trunk of a yew tree where a strong almost right-angled branch grew out. Thus the haft came from the trunk and the shaft from a branch. The natural joint between the trunk and branch gave the axe maximum durability.

EXPERTLY HAMMERED

An examination of the metal in the blade reveals it to be almost completely pure copper with traces of arsenic and silver. Pure copper is not easy to cast. When the metal contracts on cooling, bound oxygen creates small cavities or recesses and these can be seen on Ötzi's axe too, particularly on the neck. The blade was sharpened with considerable skill.

COPPER CASTING

The molten metal is poured into a stone or clay die which stands upright. After cooling, the cast is hammered and ground into shape.

Dangerous Hunting Weapons

The largest object in Ötzi's kit was his 1.82-metre-long yew longbow – a good 20 centimetres taller than its owner. This bow is not yet ready to be used as the handles and notches for mounting the cord are missing – a simple job but for Ötzi's death. Either he lost the old bow or it was no longer usable. Twelve of the fourteen arrows found in his quiver were also unfinished. Strangely enough, the two finished arrows were both broken. The quiver too was already damaged when the dead man was first covered by the snow. Evidently the bow and arrows were very important to the Iceman and he would have eventually tried to replace them with new, functioning weapons.

IN GROUPS

Neolithic man probably went big game hunting in groups. While some of them trapped the animal, the others awaited the catch with their deadly arrows. Their diet consisted of meat from bears, deer, chamois and ibex as well as small mammals, birds and fish.

BEARSKIN

It is thought that Ötzi himself may have killed the bear whose skin he used to make his cap.

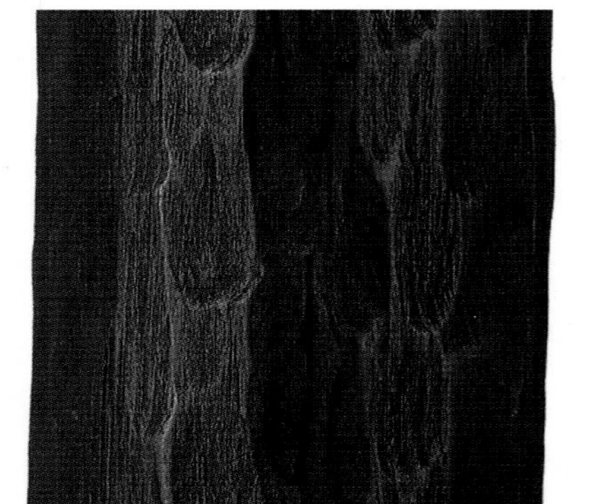

SKILLFULLY CARVED

The facetted signs of carving clearly show that the bow is unfinished. It still has to be planed, greased and the bowstring attached.

HARDWOOD

For his bow Ötzi chose the tough, resin-free, highly flexible yew. From the sharp edges of its carved facets, it can be seen how difficult it was to work this hard wood.

THE TOOL

Ötzi fashioned his bow stave out of a yew trunk using his axe and flint dagger. He then carved out a D-shaped cross-section and tapered the ends.

Section of longbow broken off during the recovery

ABSOLUTELY DEADLY

Tests have shown that using such a bow, wild animals such as brown bears could be accurately hit from a distance of 30 to 50 metres.

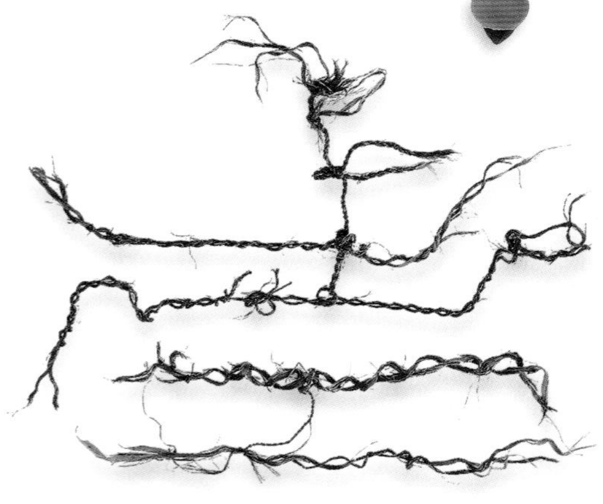

CATCHING BIRDS AND TRAPPING RABBITS

Among Ötzi's possessions was a large-meshed knotted net. It was made of grass string and probably used for catching birds. In prehistoric times such nets were also used for trapping rabbits by extending them over the entrance to the warren where they would be clubbed to death.

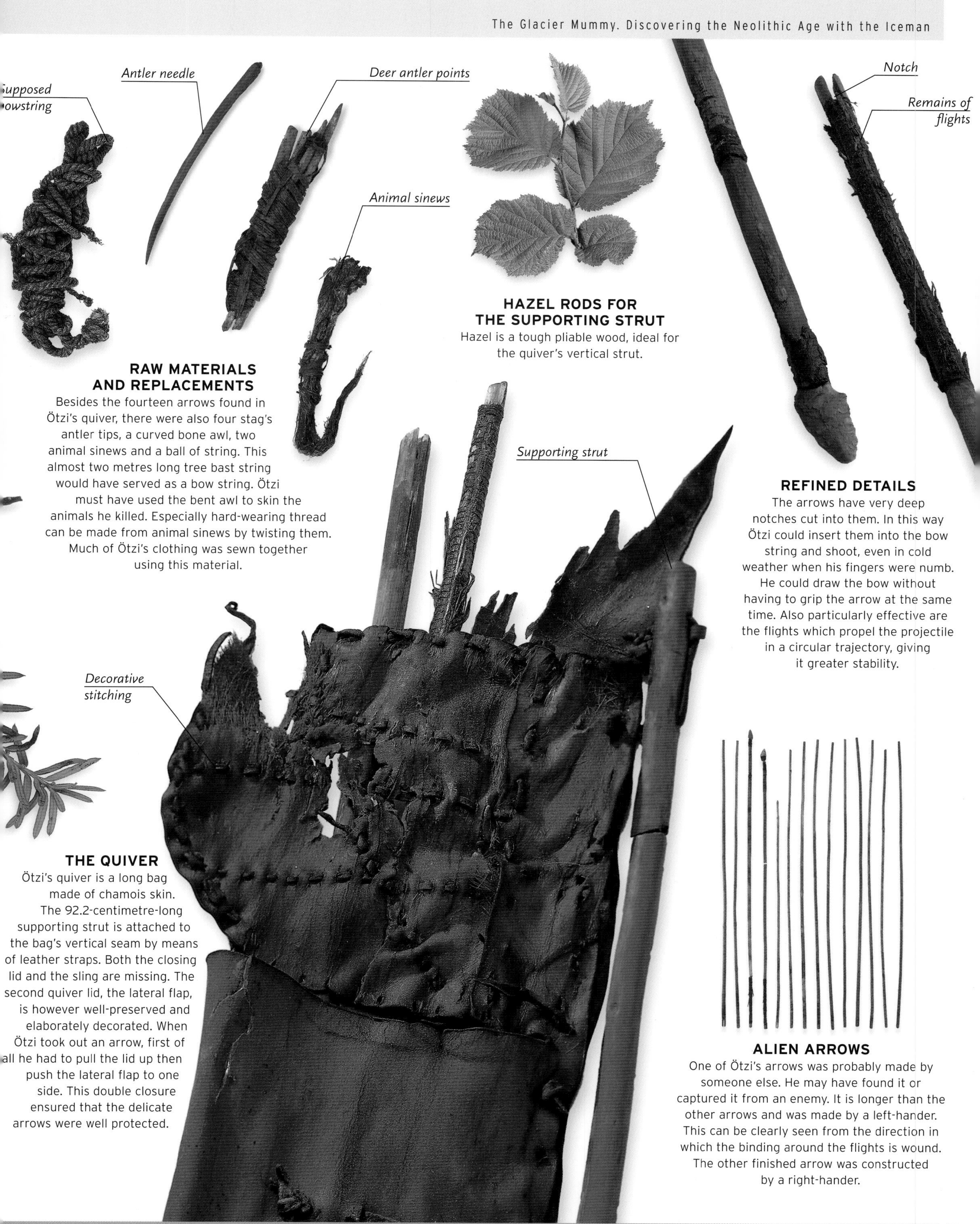

RAW MATERIALS AND REPLACEMENTS

Besides the fourteen arrows found in Ötzi's quiver, there were also four stag's antler tips, a curved bone awl, two animal sinews and a ball of string. This almost two metres long tree bast string would have served as a bow string. Ötzi must have used the bent awl to skin the animals he killed. Especially hard-wearing thread can be made from animal sinews by twisting them. Much of Ötzi's clothing was sewn together using this material.

HAZEL RODS FOR THE SUPPORTING STRUT

Hazel is a tough pliable wood, ideal for the quiver's vertical strut.

REFINED DETAILS

The arrows have very deep notches cut into them. In this way Ötzi could insert them into the bow string and shoot, even in cold weather when his fingers were numb. He could draw the bow without having to grip the arrow at the same time. Also particularly effective are the flights which propel the projectile in a circular trajectory, giving it greater stability.

THE QUIVER

Ötzi's quiver is a long bag made of chamois skin. The 92.2-centimetre-long supporting strut is attached to the bag's vertical seam by means of leather straps. Both the closing lid and the sling are missing. The second quiver lid, the lateral flap, is however well-preserved and elaborately decorated. When Ötzi took out an arrow, first of all he had to pull the lid up then push the lateral flap to one side. This double closure ensured that the delicate arrows were well protected.

ALIEN ARROWS

One of Ötzi's arrows was probably made by someone else. He may have found it or captured it from an enemy. It is longer than the other arrows and was made by a left-hander. This can be clearly seen from the direction in which the binding around the flights is wound. The other finished arrow was constructed by a right-hander.

Stone Age Technology

VIBURNUM
Most of Ötzi's arrows are made from the carved shoots of viburnum sapwood. This bush produces long, straight and extremely tough shoots.

WILD BIRD FEATHERS
The feathers for Ötzi's flights must have come from wild birds as Neolithic man had not yet domesticated these animals. Among the birds which inhabited Ötzi's environment were black woodpeckers, choughs, alpine choughs, ravens, golden eagles, black vultures, Egyptian vultures and griffon vultures.

Before his death, the Iceman was working on a new bow and several arrows. How far he got can be seen by looking at the original objects in the South Tyrol Museum of Archaeology. The bow was completely carved but not yet planed and lacked the handles, notches and bow string. Ötzi had only prepared the shafts of the twelve new arrows. To do this, he removed the bark from viburnum sapwood shoots, then cut notches into the ends and finally smoothed down the shafts. Apparently he did not work on one arrow from start to finish, instead using a form of mass-production to avoid constantly having to change tools. An archaeologist spotlights the next steps necessary for the preparation of one of Ötzi's arrows.

PRECISE PRESSURE
The point of the arrowhead is roughly hammered out using a piece of antler and then finished with the retoucheur.

STONE AGE STICKY
Birch pitch is heated until it acquires the consistency of tar. It is then daubed onto the bottom end of the arrowhead and the tip of the shaft.

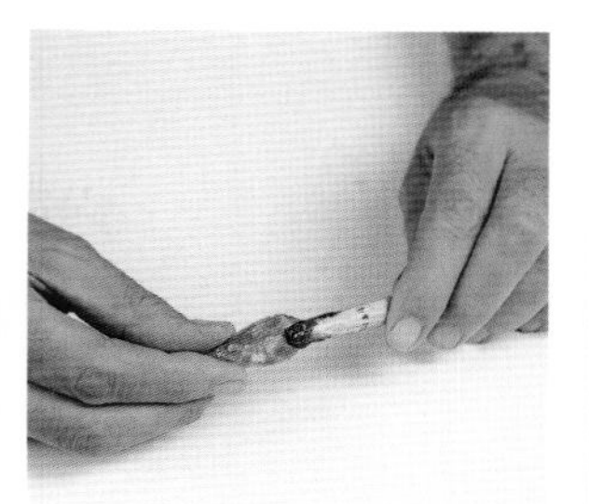

HURRY HURRY
The arrowhead must be attached straight away. When it cools, the tar becomes as hard as glass.

DOUBLE BINDING
Ötzi would then wind animal sinews round the shaft which sank into the hot birch tar.

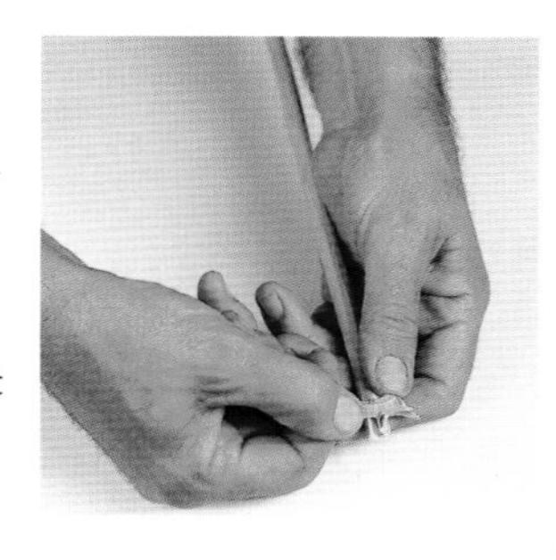

DEEP CUTS
The other end of the shaft is slightly thinned and a deep notch cut into it. For this job Ötzi probably used the small, sharp, rounded lamella he kept in his belt pouch.

SKILLFUL WORK
A sharp flintstone is used to split the quill. Then the two halves of the feather are cut into radial flights to give the arrow a deadly spin.

CAREFUL WITH THE SUPERGLUE
The three fine grooves for the flights are each 13 centimetres long. One of them is coated with heated birch tar.

FIXING THE FLIGHTS
One of the feathers is quickly but carefully pressed into the coated groove. After the tar has cooled and hardened, the two other feathers can be attached.

SUCCESS!
Finally a thread is wound round the fixed feather halves in spiral fashion using an antler awl to separate the feather fibres. Ötzi's thread was made of twisted nettle fibres.

The Birch-Bark Containers

PUZZLE
Out of these meagre pieces, specialists at the Römisch-Germanisches Zentralmuseum at Mainz, Germany, partially reconstructed Ötzi's 20-centimetre-high birch-bark containers.

Archaeologists work rather like detectives. The smallest clue is carefully examined and compared with other finds. Everything, including items that were originally thought to be irrelevant, is assembled so that the puzzle can be solved or a new hypothesis put forward. This is what happened with the dry, extremely fragile pieces of birch bark found on the Tisenjoch which were trampled on and strewn by the wind. They were collected and documented, preserved and restored and finally of course, thoroughly examined with modern technology. Today, thanks to this research, we know to which objects these pieces belong, their shape and their use. More importantly they tell us where Ötzi had been before he died and in which season his death occurred.

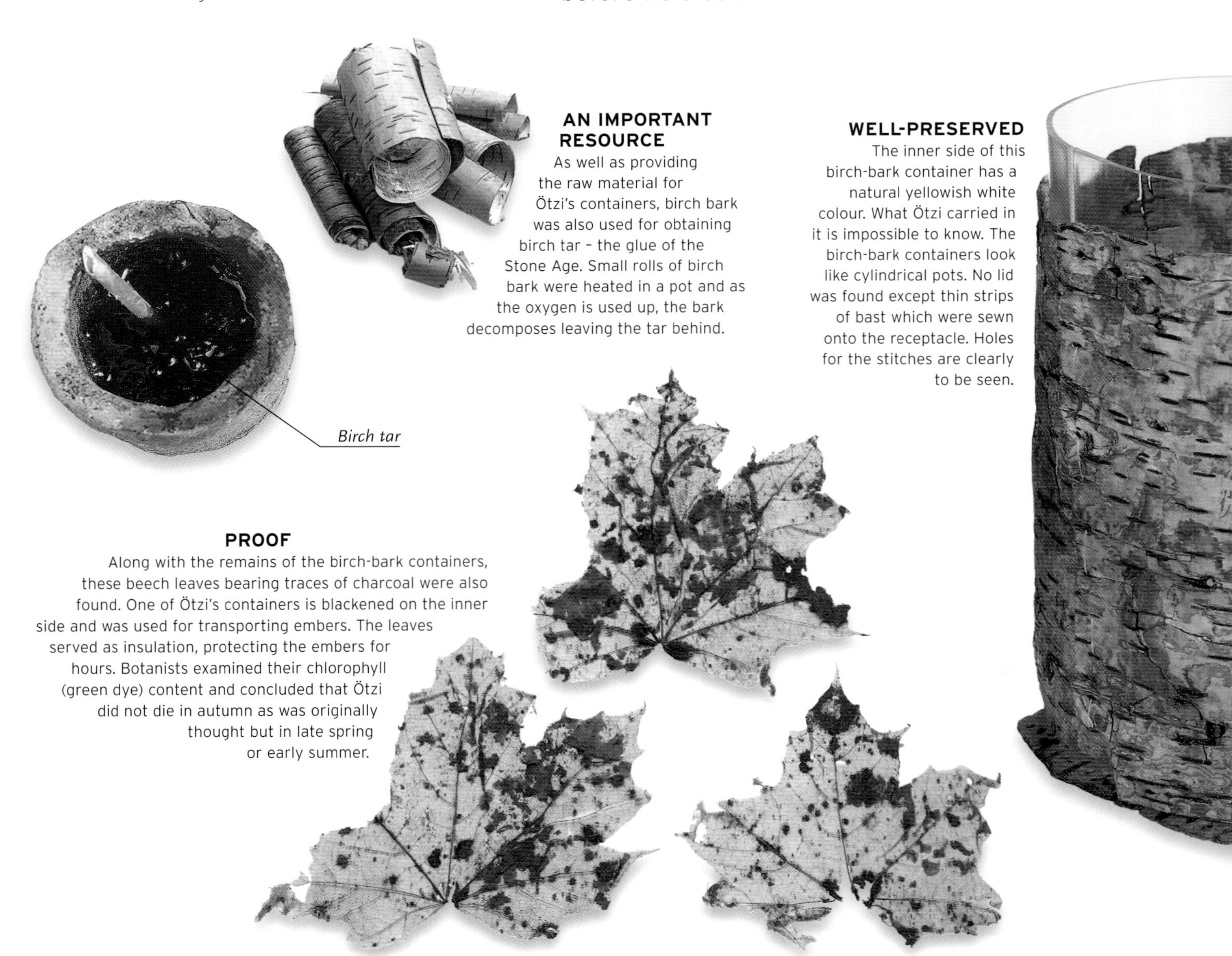

AN IMPORTANT RESOURCE
As well as providing the raw material for Ötzi's containers, birch bark was also used for obtaining birch tar – the glue of the Stone Age. Small rolls of birch bark were heated in a pot and as the oxygen is used up, the bark decomposes leaving the tar behind.

WELL-PRESERVED
The inner side of this birch-bark container has a natural yellowish white colour. What Ötzi carried in it is impossible to know. The birch-bark containers look like cylindrical pots. No lid was found except thin strips of bast which were sewn onto the receptacle. Holes for the stitches are clearly to be seen.

PROOF
Along with the remains of the birch-bark containers, these beech leaves bearing traces of charcoal were also found. One of Ötzi's containers is blackened on the inner side and was used for transporting embers. The leaves served as insulation, protecting the embers for hours. Botanists examined their chlorophyll (green dye) content and concluded that Ötzi did not die in autumn as was originally thought but in late spring or early summer.

Spruce

Cherry dogwood

Juniper

SIGNS OF A CLIMB

The charcoal particles on the beech leaves derive from six different types of wood. Among them are traces of elm (Ulmus sp.) which is only found in lowlands and net-leafed willow which grows above the timber-line. Ötzi and his campfire therefore must have moved up in stages from the valley floor to the heights of the mountains.

FURTHER PROOF

Besides the tiny charcoal particles, the beech leaves were also embedded with spruce (Picea abies) and juniper (Juniperus sp.) needles as well as husks of einkorn (Triticum monococcum) and wheat (Triticum sp.), providing evidence that Ötzi came from a cereal growing society. The types of wood used for the manufacture of his equipment offer further clues: one of Ötzi's arrows was apparently made of cherry dogwood, a tree which principally grows south of the Alps.

Pinewood charcoal chips were also found in the ember containers

Stitch holes

THE EMBER POT

The inner side of this container came into contact with coal and ashes and is therefore blackened. Ötzi would carry the remains of his previous campfire with him so that he could light the next one quickly and effortlessly.

DISAPPOINTMENT FOR THE ARCHAEOLOGISTS

Ötzi had no ceramic vessels with him - the light birch-bark containers are much more effective for high mountain travel than heavy, breakable pottery. Since prehistoric cultures are categorised according to the ceramics they leave behind, archaeologists were denied an important classification criterion in the case of Ötzi. His exact place of origin therefore remains unknown.

Experiments with Fire

POWERFUL BLOWS
By hitting a piece of iron pyrites, an extremely hard rock, against the side of a flintstone, sparks start to fly. However, even experienced fire-starters cannot achieve this effect straight away.

For the Iceman and his contemporaries, the mastery of fire was essential for their survival. It offered protection from the cold and wild animals, made meat and other foods more pleasant and more easily digestible and enabled the production of metal and ceramic objects. Fire was also used for clearing forest in order to make settlements bigger. As an uncontrollable, destructive element, fire also played an important role in the prehistoric system of worship. The difficulty of making fire, especially in wet weather, led early man to conserve embers beneath a layer of ashes or earth in order to be able to light a new fire with ease. For those like Ötzi who were often on the move, embers could be transported wrapped in fresh grass or leaves. And if the ashes went out, there was always the option of the firelighter. Ötzi carried a piece of a prehistoric flint firelighter in his belt pouch. The effectiveness of such a firelighter can be convincingly demonstrated.

A SHOWER OF SPARKS
As soon as a spark lands on a crumbled piece of true-tinder fungus it begins to glow.

HARDER THAN GOLD
Tiny, shiny, light yellow pyrite crystals were discovered in Ötzi's true-tinder fungus. Although iron pyrites, also known as fool's gold, were not found in Ötzi's belt pouch, the traces found in the true-tinder show that he must have carried this material at some point.

SOFT AND FLUFFY
Ötzi's true-tinder fungus was prepared in advance, in a way similar to that used up to modern times. The soft flesh of the tree fungus is cut into pieces and soaked in a saltpetre solution. In prehistoric times, urine was probably used instead. The inflammability of organic materials can be increased when they are mixed with nitrogen, present in both saltpetre and urine. Before being used, the well-dried tinder is rubbed until it becomes fibrous and fluffy like cotton wool.

FUSS-FREE FIRE
Making fire with a flint fire lighter is time-consuming and only works in open air when the weather is dry. In wet weather the true-tinder fungus, hay, leaves and twigs become too damp. For just such conditions Ötzi carried his ember container.

EASY TO LIGHT
Various materials are suitable for tinder, but the best is the true-tinder fungus (Fomes fomentarius). A type of polypore, this fungus appears on sick or dying beech trees, growing to a size of up to 30 centimetres.

ONLY THE FLESH
Only a part of the true-tinder fungus is used as tinder - the upper crust and the lower layer of tubiflora flesh. In the Stone Age, it would be cut from the whole fungus using a sharp flint blade or lamella.

ON THE HEARTH
The ember hearth is placed on a pile of hay and gently blown.

FEEDING THE FLAMES
Soon the pile is set alight and more light, flammable material can be added.

TORCH-LIKE
Leaves and small twigs are placed on the burning pile of hay and further blown until the whole pile is ablaze. The experiment is a total success!

Selected Raw Materials

Ötzi's clothing and equipment consist principally of organic materials such as leather, wood and grass. All these materials were carefully chosen and tell us a great deal about the Iceman's environment. It is astonishing the number of uses these materials were put to. It seems that the most appropriate material for each piece of clothing and equipment was chosen. People in the Neolithic Age possessed an extraordinarily detailed knowledge of their environment, something which has been largely lost by modern civilisation.

FEARFUL PREDATORS

The raw materials for Ötzi's clothing came from both domestic and wild animals. Bears, stags and chamois had to be hunted. The feathers for his arrow flights also came from wild birds since none had been domesticated at that time. From the hide of the brown bear (Ursus arctos), caps and shoe soles were made.

NIMBLE CLIMBERS

The hide of the chamois (Rupicapra rupicapra) was used in the making of the quiver. The small awl found in Ötzi's belt pouch probably came from one of these animals' bones.

HUNTED OR COLLECTED

The red deer (Cervus elaphus) provided the point of the retoucheur, the large curved awl and the four antler tips. However it is impossible to say if they were made from discarded pieces Ötzi found or came from an animal he himself had hunted and killed.

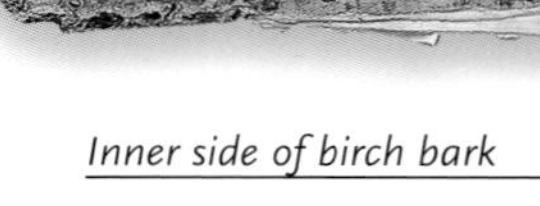

Inner side of birch bark

IMPORTANT LIVESTOCK

The many uses of goatskin – the leather coat, the loin cloth and leggings – proves that livestock breeding was important to Ötzi. The goat (Capra hircus), along with the dog (Canis familiaris), the sheep (Ovis aries), the pig (Sus domesticus) and the cow (Bos taurus) are the five classic domestic animals of Late Stone Age Central Europe. To the north of the Alps, cattle and pigs were more common while to the south, sheep and goats were preferred.

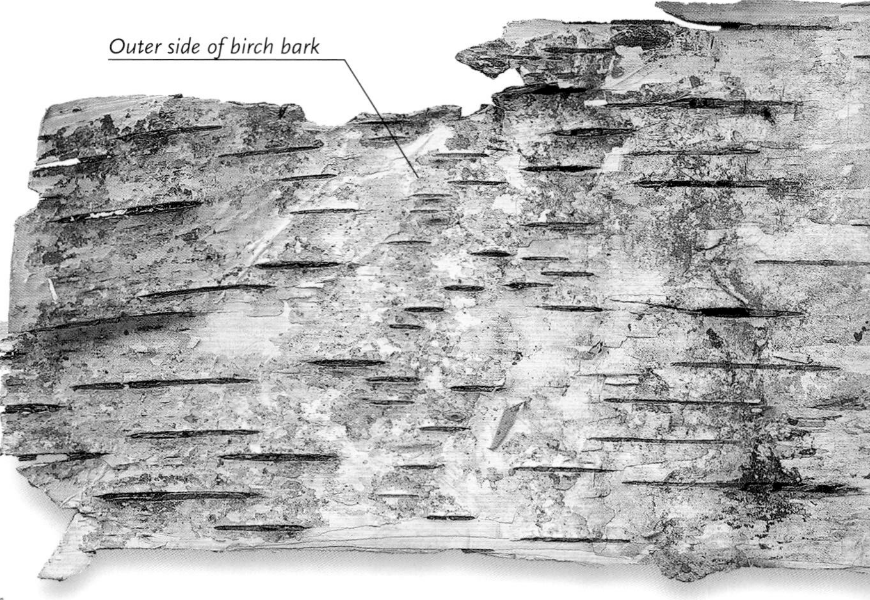

Outer side of birch bark

A SOURCE OF TIMBER AND BAST

A piece of a branch from a lime tree (Tilia sp.) was fashioned by Ötzi into the stub of his retoucheur. Ötzi also wound and twisted the fibres of lime bast into thread and string. These were used to tie up the antler tips and the sinews found in his quiver.

WIDELY AVAILABLE

Ötzi carried two birch-bark containers with him. In prehistoric times, the birch tree (Betula sp.) was not only treasured as a provider of "glue": it was also ideal for making containers and cases. The bark of young trees is easy to strip, flexible and very resistant when dried.

NATURAL INSULATION

Ötzi used the leaves of the Norwegian maple tree (Acer platanoides) as insulation for his embers. This tree was not found in the northern Alps in Ötzi's time. It is characterised by its hand-shaped pointed leaves.

STRAIGHT AS AN ARROW

The thin stems of the viburnum or wayfaring tree (Viburnum lantana) are incredibly straight. For this reason most of Ötzi's arrow shafts were carved from them.

FLEXIBLE

The flexible rods from the hazel (Corylus avellana) were used in prehistoric times for the lattice framework of mud walls and for the curved inner structure of ovens. Hazel wood was also used for the U-shaped frame of Ötzi's back pack and the vertical strut of his quiver.

Serviceberry

TWO KINDS OF WOOD

The longest of Ötzi's two finished arrows is a so-called composite arrow. This means that the wooden shaft is composed of two sections. The shorter front section is not made of viburnum sapwood like the other arrow shafts, but either of dogwood (Cornus sanguinea) or cherry dogwood (Cornus mas). Dogwood is found both north and south of the Alps while cherry dogwood, with the exception of the area round Lake Constance, only grows to the south of the watershed – in the eastern Vinschgau area of the South Tyrol near Merano and the surroundings of Bolzano.

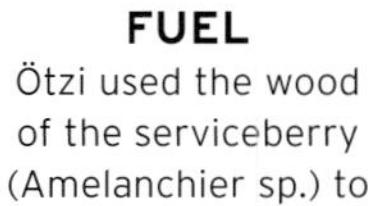

FUEL

Ötzi used the wood of the serviceberry (Amelanchier sp.) to make fire.

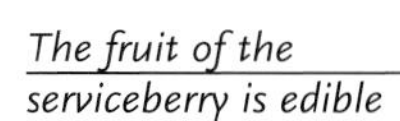

The fruit of the serviceberry is edible

WORLD CLASS WOOD

While in prehistoric times, yew (Taxus baccata) was almost exclusively employed for making longbows, Ötzi also used it for the haft of his axe. Yew does not rot nor exude sap and is very heavy. The tree prefers south-facing, mid-mountain territory with mild winters.

GRASS FABRIC

These wetland grasses are similar to the reed sweetgrass (Glyceria maxima) which was plaited to make Ötzi's grass matting. They exist in high Alpine regions and grow to a substantial length.

Dating

THE FIRST HIEROGLYPHICS

Ötzi lived over 5,000 years ago. At that time hieroglyphics already existed and the first Kingdoms of the Pharaohs had been established.

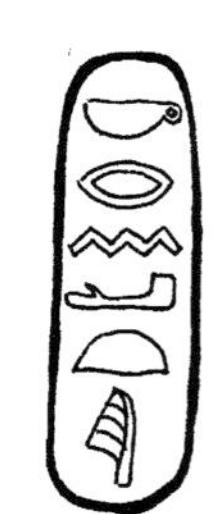

During the days that followed his discovery, estimates of the Iceman's age steadily rose. The discoverers of the corpse reckoned it was ten to twenty years old and later it was thought to be the body of the victim of a mountaineering accident from the time of the Second World War. Every time the corpse was seen, estimates of his age rose by hundreds of years until the archaeologist Konrad Spindler made the astonishing estimate of at least 4,000 years. Radiocarbon dating - the scientific process for measuring radioactive decomposition - finally brought conclusive proof. The findings of the so-called carbon-14 method were subjected to another age calculation test: dendrochronology or tree ring dating. This proved conclusively that Ötzi lived between 3,350 and 3,100 years BC.

OLDER THAN EGYPTIAN MUMMIES

Ötzi had already been in his icy grave for 500 years before Stonehenge was erected. A further 100 years later, Cheops had the Great Pyramid built. When the Egyptian art of embalming reached its peak around 1,000 BC, Ötzi had already been dead for over 2,000 years.

C-14 reaches animals and humans through the food chain

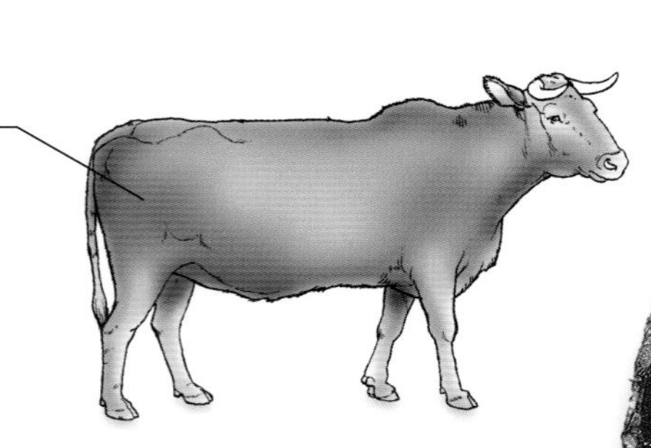

RADIOCARBON DATING

Cosmic ray neutrons entering the earth's atmosphere convert nitrogen into radioactive carbon-14 isotopes. These reach plants through photosynthesis and people and animals through the food chain. When a living thing dies, the flow of carbon-14 is interrupted and the carbon isotope is very slowly diminished. After 5,730 years half of it is still present, after a further 5,730 years a quarter and so on. In this way, the age of a given sample can be calculated by the remaining number of radioactive carbon isotopes. In order to make a calculation, the sample must be prepared since the number of C-14 isotopes in a living being is extremely low. For example proteins are extracted from a bone particle and converted into benzol. Variations in atmospheric C-14 concentrations make the radiocarbon dating of items over 1,000 years somewhat inaccurate. This problem is countered using dendochronology, or tree ring dating, which corrects the errors of the carbon-14 method.

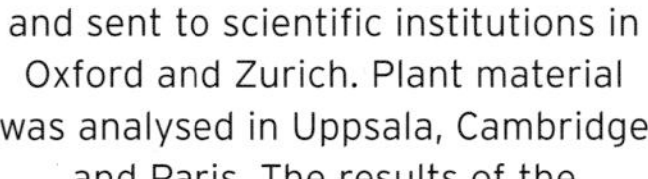

FIVE LABS - ONE FIND

To carry out the carbon-14 research, tiny bone particles and tissue fibres were taken from the damaged left hip and sent to scientific institutions in Oxford and Zurich. Plant material was analysed in Uppsala, Cambridge and Paris. The results of the independent tests carried out by laboratories in Britain, Switzerland, Sweden and France all gave Ötzi the same age.

Inorganic material

IDEAL CONDITIONS

Only organic materials such as bones, plants or leather are suitable for radiocarbon dating. Artefacts made of inorganic materials which contain no atmospheric carbon particles such as metal, stone or ceramics cannot be dated using the carbon-14 method. Therefore the Tisenjoch find was ideal for this type of analysis.

Organic material

FRAGMENTS AS INDICATORS

Ceramics are an important key for dating. Their shape, decoration and production techniques are constantly subject to enormous variations and changing fashions. This is just as true of Neolithic times as it is today. Archaeologists are familiar with the tell-tale signs that distinguish ceramics from a particular period or area. By comparing a fragment with already known datable pottery, they are able to calculate its age. Much to the disappointment of archaeologists, no ceramic items were found with Ötzi.

DENDROCHRONOLOGY

Tree ring dating is founded on the idea that tree trunks in moderate climatic zones annually grow a new ring. With low rainfall these rings are narrower while wet weather makes them grow wider. With this process it is possible to determine age far into the past by finding a comparable sequence in the width of the distance between rings, as shown here in a curve diagram.

The width of tree rings depends on the climate

STEP BY STEP BACK INTO PREHISTORY

By taking growth curves from increasingly old wood samples – starting with, for example, freshly felled trees, then modern roof beams, then medieval bridges, Roman ships and so on – and placing them on top of each other in their corresponding positions, the sequence can be prolonged further and further into the past. The tree ring calendar goes as far back as 10,000 years.

WIDE – NARROW

The width of the year rings is measured under a microscope and converted into a scale. A computer compares the curves and looks in the year ring calendar for similar sequences of broad and narrow annual rings.

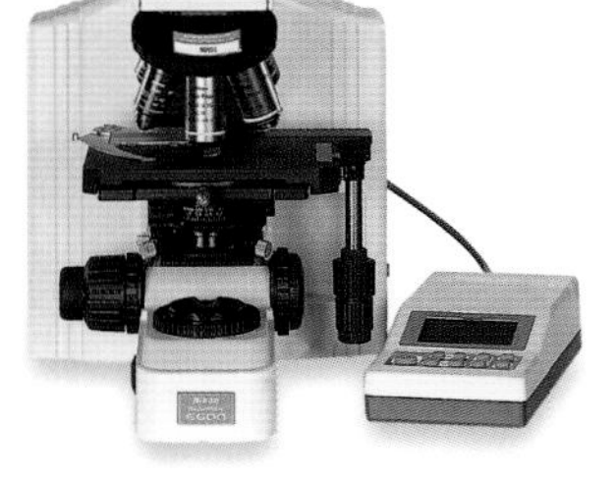

SUITABLE SAMPLES

In order to be able to fit a wood sample into the annual ring calendar, a sequence must consist of over 50 annual rings. Among Ötzi's wooden objects, the longbow has the largest number of annual rings. For the time being however this is not enough to determine its age. With the dendochronological method, C-14 data can be simply corrected.

Conservation and Restoration

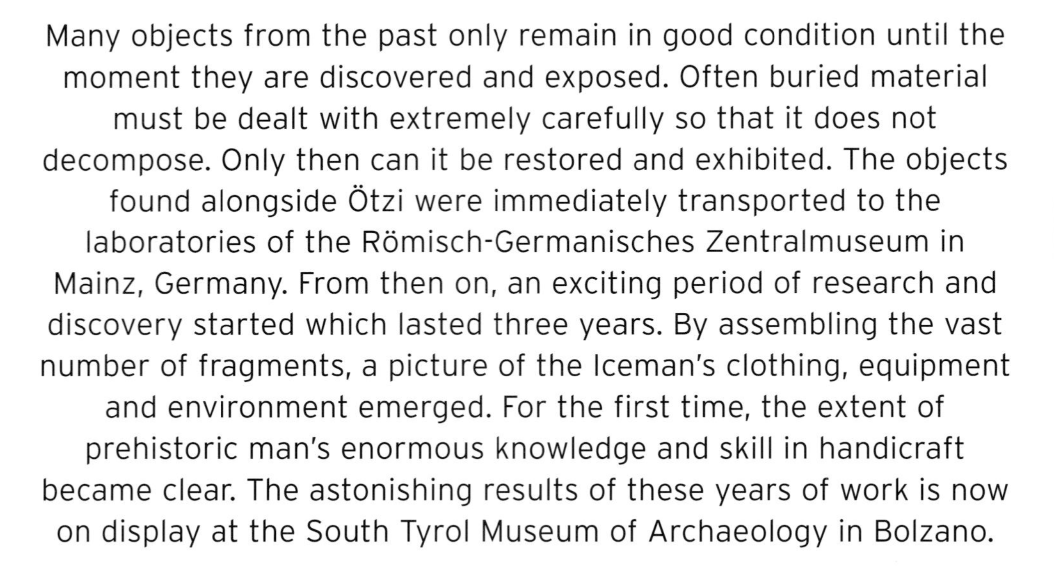

Many objects from the past only remain in good condition until the moment they are discovered and exposed. Often buried material must be dealt with extremely carefully so that it does not decompose. Only then can it be restored and exhibited. The objects found alongside Ötzi were immediately transported to the laboratories of the Römisch-Germanisches Zentralmuseum in Mainz, Germany. From then on, an exciting period of research and discovery started which lasted three years. By assembling the vast number of fragments, a picture of the Iceman's clothing, equipment and environment emerged. For the first time, the extent of prehistoric man's enormous knowledge and skill in handicraft became clear. The astonishing results of these years of work is now on display at the South Tyrol Museum of Archaeology in Bolzano.

ALL PILED UP
At the time of Ötzi's recovery, most of his clothing looked like a pile of old rags - scraps of leather, bits of plaited material and clumps of hair.

EXPOSED TO THE ELEMENTS
Some items of his equipment lay on a higher rocky shelf and emerged from the ice before the corpse. They were therefore exposed to the damaging effects of night frosts, variations in humidity and ultra-violet rays for much longer.

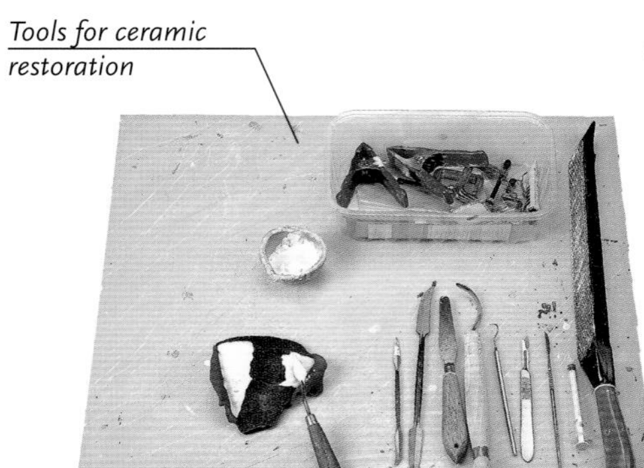

Tools for ceramic restoration

GAP FILLING
The missing parts of clay pots are replaced by plaster (complementary measures). The empty space on the inside is covered with wax and crepe adhesive tape and finally filled with plaster. As soon as the plaster is dry, it is polished and painted. Restoration should be inconspicuous but, on close inspection, also be visible so that the differences between the replacements and the original fragments can be seen.

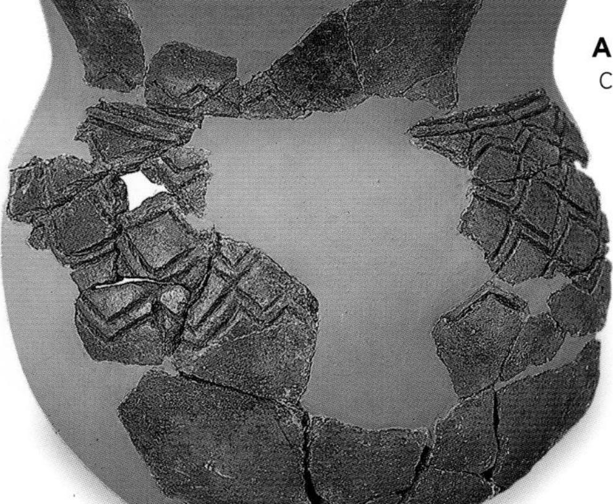

A RESTORED CLAY POT
Ceramics are the most common objects found at archaeological digs. Like stone and gold, they survive thousands of years. However most buried pottery is found in incomplete fragments. Often a sufficient number of pieces remain to permit the reconstruction of the original form of the receptacle. In order to do so, the pieces are cleaned and pieced together like a jigsaw.

Pieces glued together are left to dry in a sand tray

STEAMING
Special care was required for the reconstruction of Ötzi's birch-bark containers. On arrival at the restoration labs in Mainz, the few remaining pieces were totally dried out and extremely fragile. By the use of steam, the pieces regained their flexibility, making it possible to reconstruct their original form.

Nylon thread

SUPPORTING THREAD
Ötzi's 'cans' are made of a single, square-cut piece of bark. The two perforated edges were overlapped and sewn together. The lower part of the container was also sewn on to the oval base in the same way. Since none of the original thread remained, nylon twine was used for the restoration (supporting measures). This can always be removed - any restoration must have the capacity to be reversed.

SPECIALIST RECOVERY

Ötzi's bearskin cap was found in August 1992, at the foot of the stone slab where he lay, surrounded by ice. With the aid of a steam jet and the constant drainage of the snowmelt, the find was carefully removed from the ice and documented in drawings, film and photographs.

STEADY HANDS

Restorers spend a lot of time looking through the microscope. Beneath the magnifying glass they use scalpels, tweezers and other tools which require great care and patience.

SPECIALIST TRANSPORT

After its recovery, the partially frozen cap was packed in a sterilised plastic bag. It was then quickly transported to the Ancient Monuments Office in Bolzano in a cooled light metal case and placed in a refrigerator before being sent on to Mainz.

DOCUMENTATION

During the examination of any find, artefacts are photographed several times. After they have been restored, scale drawings of the objects are prepared along with detailed written descriptions.

HIDE OR LEATHER?

With the exception of his bearskin cap, most of the fur from Ötzi's other hide garments has almost completely fallen out. It was therefore not always easy to confirm whether an individual find was made of hide (simply stripped skin) or leather (stripped, the fur removed and tanned). Traces of scraping on the fleshy side provided important evidence. Before tanning, the remains of fat and tissue would be removed from a skinned hide with a scraper – and Ötzi possessed just such a tool. Once the type of animal and the preparation technique of each fragment had been established, they could be pieced together to reveal the shape, use and pattern of each garment.

The scraper from Ötzi's belt pouch

ÖTZI'S BEARSKIN CAP TODAY

Thanks to the care taken during the recovery, the fur on the bearskin cap remained intact – it would have fallen out at the slightest contact. In Mainz the cap was handled with special care. After cleaning it with distilled water, it was greased, soaked in a chemical substance, freeze-dried and finally restored.

The chin straps were already broken before Ötzi's death

Plants and Ötzi's Diet

The Iceman lived in a time of radical changes which originated in the Middle East and drastically altered the lives of people in Europe: the transition from a hunter-gatherer society to agriculture and livestock breeding. This so-called Neolithic Revolution had wide-ranging consequences. People settled to cultivate and protect the land and build more permanent houses. At the same time ceramics came into use. The transition to agriculture and livestock breeding paved the way for the division of labour and, consequently, the accumulation of surplus stocks and private property. The Alpine area was heavily settled during the Copper Age as its rich mineral deposits enabled local tribes to make considerable economic and cultural progress. As a result, agricultural land had to be extended and cultivation became more intensive. Fruit gathering, however, provided a welcome addition to people's diets.

FINE FRUITS
Raspberries (Rubus idaeus), blackberries (Rubus fruticosus), rosehip (Rosa sp.), elderberries (Sambucus sp.) and sloeberries (Prunus spinosa) were all collected and stored to vary and enrich the daily diet.

A BERRY A DAY KEEPS THE DOCTOR AWAY
Due to their high fruit acid and bitter essence content, sloeberries are today only edible raw after the first frost. Around the large pip lies a thin layer of fruit, so the sloeberry is not a particularly satisfying food but rather a source of vitamins and minerals. When it is chewed, saliva flow increases thus warding off thirst.

Wild plums were dried and stored for winter

Wild apples (Malus silvestris) were mainly dried

EDIBLE MUSHROOMS
Tree fungus was collected as tinder material and for its therapeutic effects and edible mushrooms, as their name suggests, for eating.

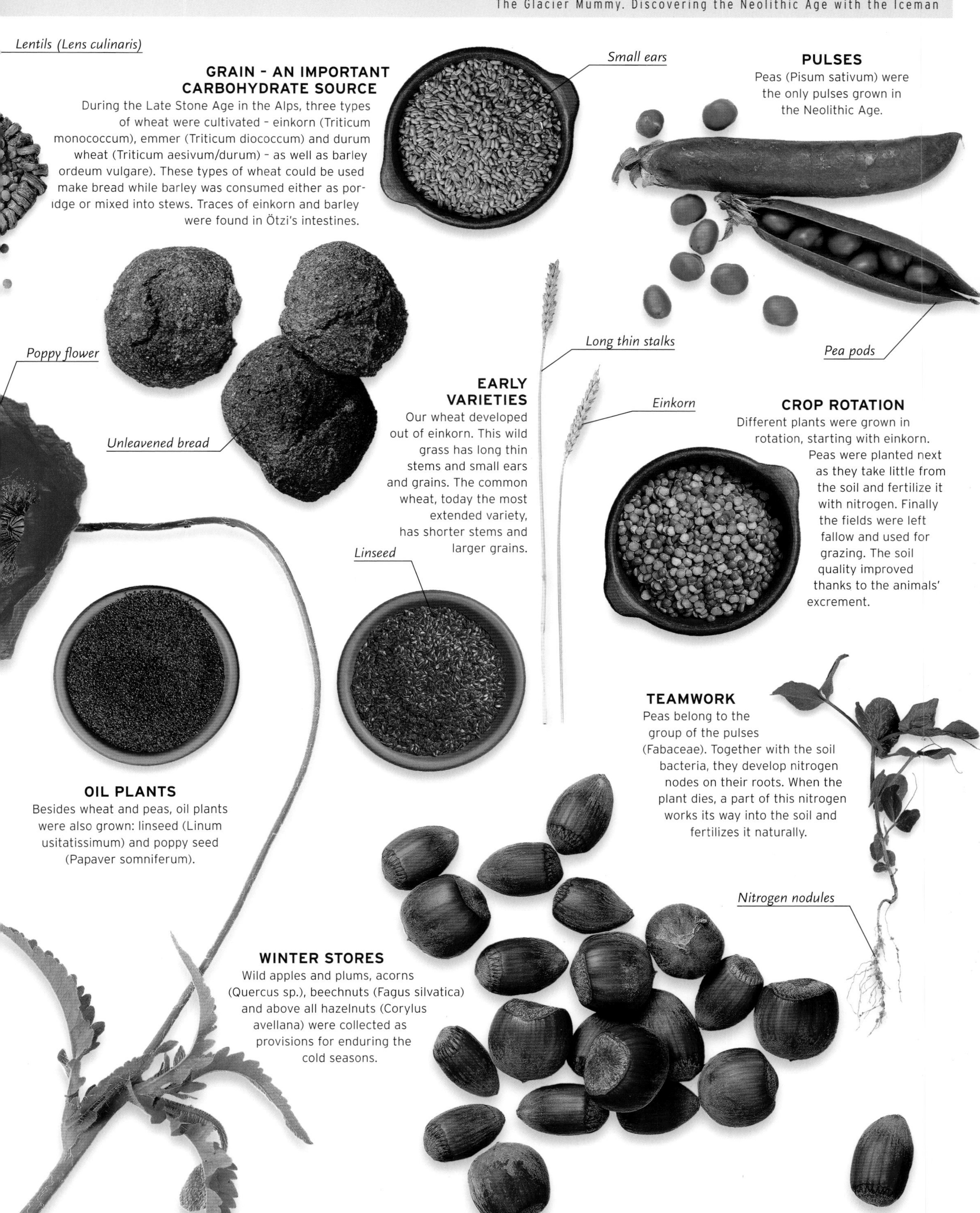

GRAIN - AN IMPORTANT CARBOHYDRATE SOURCE

During the Late Stone Age in the Alps, three types of wheat were cultivated - einkorn (Triticum monococcum), emmer (Triticum diococcum) and durum wheat (Triticum aesivum/durum) - as well as barley ordeum vulgare). These types of wheat could be used make bread while barley was consumed either as poridge or mixed into stews. Traces of einkorn and barley were found in Ötzi's intestines.

PULSES

Peas (Pisum sativum) were the only pulses grown in the Neolithic Age.

EARLY VARIETIES

Our wheat developed out of einkorn. This wild grass has long thin stems and small ears and grains. The common wheat, today the most extended variety, has shorter stems and larger grains.

CROP ROTATION

Different plants were grown in rotation, starting with einkorn. Peas were planted next as they take little from the soil and fertilize it with nitrogen. Finally the fields were left fallow and used for grazing. The soil quality improved thanks to the animals' excrement.

TEAMWORK

Peas belong to the group of the pulses (Fabaceae). Together with the soil bacteria, they develop nitrogen nodes on their roots. When the plant dies, a part of this nitrogen works its way into the soil and fertilizes it naturally.

OIL PLANTS

Besides wheat and peas, oil plants were also grown: linseed (Linum usitatissimum) and poppy seed (Papaver somniferum).

WINTER STORES

Wild apples and plums, acorns (Quercus sp.), beechnuts (Fagus silvatica) and above all hazelnuts (Corylus avellana) were collected as provisions for enduring the cold seasons.

How did Ötzi Die?

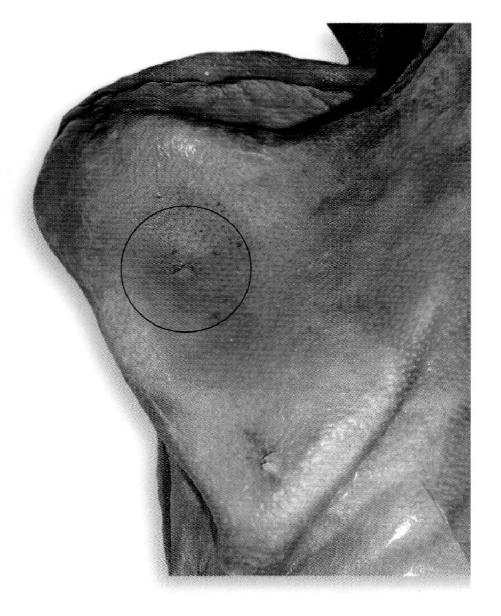

How did the Iceman die? It has taken ten years to find a satisfactory response to this frequently asked question. And this we owe to a purely chance discovery. Early in 2001, Ötzi was taken from his resting place for further scientific tests. At the Bolzano Regional Hospital, the Iceman was scanned using both computer tomography and X-ray apparatus. On examining the area of his left shoulder, doctors were astounded to discover the presence of an arrowhead. This projectile had torn through Ötzi's shoulder blade and embedded itself in his rib cage, 15 millimetres from his lung. It is likely that Ötzi himself pulled the arrow out of his back, but the head remained lodged in his body. He then surely bled to death. Whatever future scientific or forensic tests may unearth, one thing is for sure: the identity of Ötzi's murderer will forever remain a secret.

DISCOVERED BY CHANCE
A small wrinkled skin wound discovered on his back is further proof that the Iceman was shot in the back.

WAS ÖTZI BURIED?
Ötzi's equipment was visibly damaged and unfinished. There are many theories about why his longbow and most of his arrows were half-finished and the remaining arrows and the quiver damaged. One explanation was the so-called burial theory: Ötzi was buried in the place of his death along with funereal offerings in the form of unfinished and deliberately damaged weapons for his final journey. Another was Konrad Spindler's "disaster theory"

SHOT IN THE BACK
The arrow must have been shot by someone standing well behind Ötzi to his left. There is no way Ötzi could have inflicted this wound on himself, by for example, falling on to an upright arrow. An arrow can only penetrate a human body without breaking when it flies at extremely high speed.

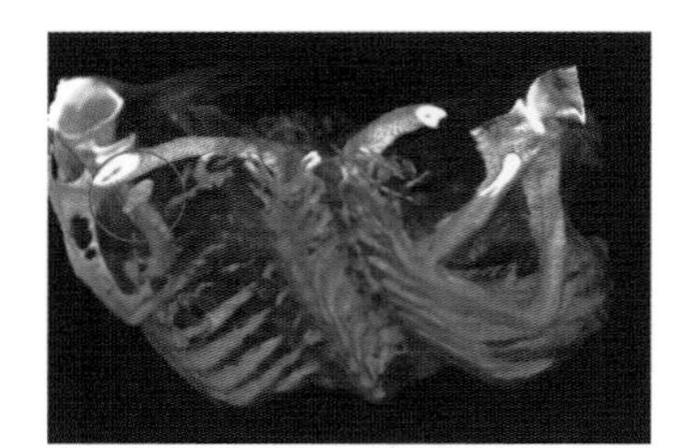

A DISASTER?
A possible scenario: as a result of a violent quarrel, Ötzi was forced to flee his village. This may have been due to a power struggle or an external attack during which Ötzi lost part of his possessions and others were damaged. He had to get himself to safety and repair his equipment as soon as possible. During this flight he died. Evidence for this theory comes from the results of an examination of his fingernails. They show chipped nails, possibly the result of fighting, as well as the three clearly marked beau lines, a well-known indicator of stress, indicating that the last weeks of the Iceman's life were particularly trying.

WHY DID ÖTZI'S BODY REMAIN UNSCATHED?

The conservation of Ötzi's corpse is the result of an unbelievable chain of events. Ötzi died at 3,210 metres above sea-level. Shortly after his death, it started to snow and his body was covered and freeze-dried. If not, his body would have been eaten by animals or simply decayed. Over the centuries the snow grew thicker and at some point, the tip of the nearby glacier slid over Ötzi. However, his frozen body was not worn away but was protected in the three-metre-deep rocky gully which lay at right-angles to the glacier's directional flow. In 1991, the glacier melted considerably. Very little snow fell that winter and the following summer was unusually hot. Strong winds had also blown large quantities of Saharan dust over the Alps. This dark desert dust absorbed the sunlight and speeded up the melting of the ice. The Iceman lay very near to a well-trodden mountain path. When Mr and Mrs Simon left this path to find a shortcut, they ended up discovering the dead man. The head and upper torso were visible and had only been exposed to the damaging rays of the sun for a short time.

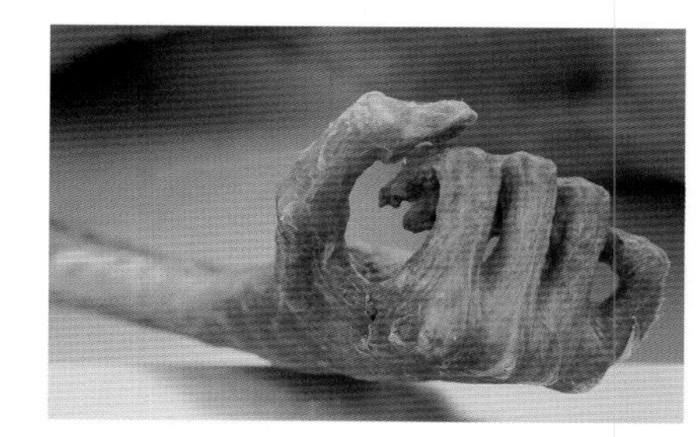

ÖTZI'S DEATH - A CRIMINAL CASE

It is clear that Ötzi was shot from behind. Other questions however remain unclear. Why was he shot? Was anything stolen from him? A herd maybe? Was this a power struggle? A deep cut on his right hand indicates that Ötzi was involved in hand-to-hand fighting shortly before his death.

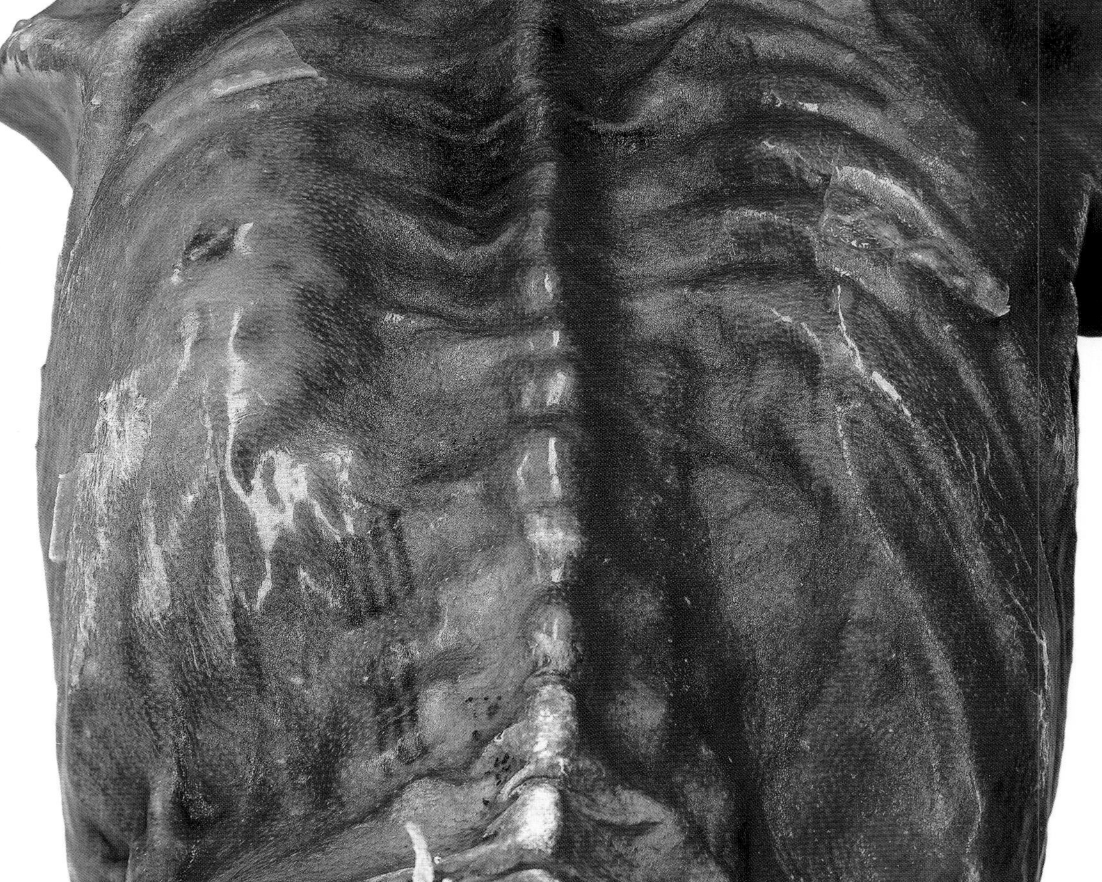

HIDDEN FOR TEN YEARS

When Spindler put forward his "disaster theory", he knew nothing of the arrowhead lodged in Ötzi's left shoulder. When the corpse was first X-rayed after its discovery in autumn 1991, no-one noticed this small foreign body. Nor was much attention paid to the tiny skin wound on his back. It was taken for one of the many injuries the Iceman suffered during his recovery from the ice.

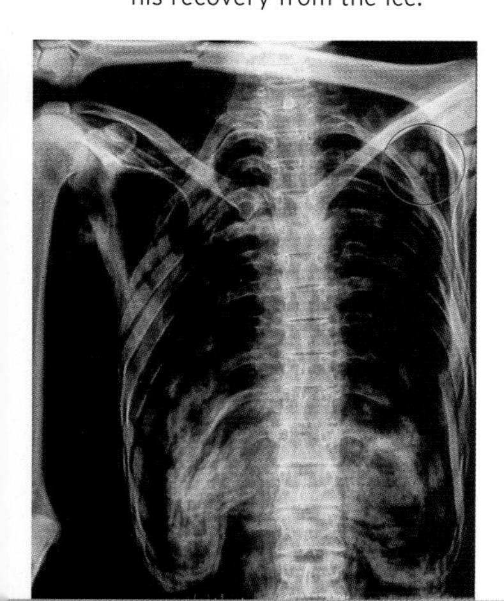

Where did Ötzi Come From?

Three sources provide conclusive proof about Ötzi's origins: the pollen in his stomach, the wooden objects found beside him and his tooth enamel. All three indicate that Ötzi lived in what is today the South Tyrol. It is more difficult to classify the Iceman as a member of a specific Late Stone Age cultural group as he carried no ceramic objects with him. Clues have emerged that point towards an entirely different source group: two carved stone objects - so-called menhir statues - suggest a close connection with the Remedello culture of Northern Italy.

RECORDED IN HIS TOOTH ENAMEL

In order to determine where Ötzi spent his childhood, researchers analysed his teeth. By comparing minerals present in his tooth enamel with water samples from the area around the scene of the find, they concluded that Ötzi must have grown up in the Eisack Valley (South Tyrol).

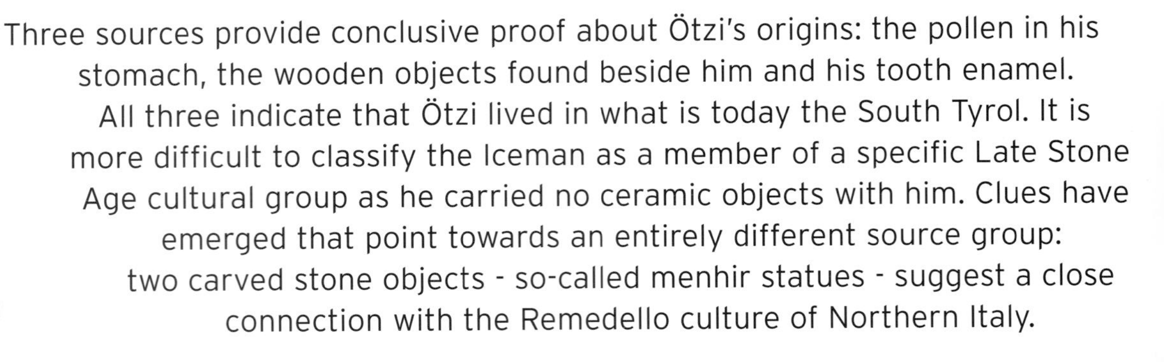

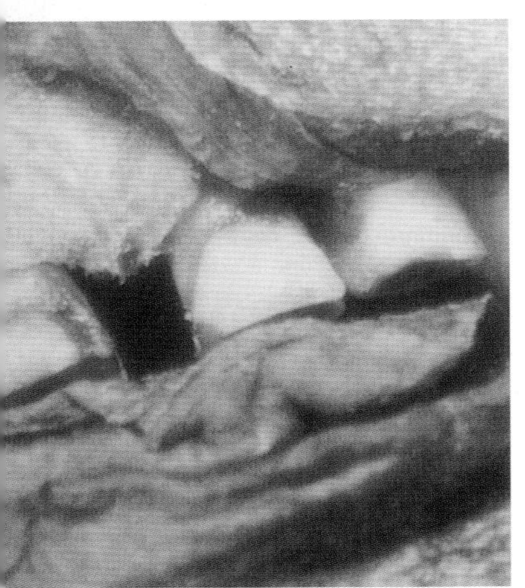

OVER THE HILLS

Close to the Hauslabjoch in the Upper Ötz Valley, there are extensive pastures which were already used for grazing in Ötzi's time. During the Copper Age, the valley floor was still so thickly wooded that thousands of sheep and goats from the Venosta Valley had to be lead up to the high pastures north of the main Alpine range in spring and brought back to the lowlands before the onset of winter. This type of long distance droving, involving the movement of entire herds, is known as transhumance. Even today, the farmers of the Senales Valley drive their sheep over the border into Austria to the high pastures of the Ötz Valley. This is the same route the Iceman took on his final journey.

ÖTZI'S LAST SUPPER

Examination of Ötzi's stomach contents provides information on ancient eating habits. Ötzi's last meal consisted of an einkorn porridge, red deer meat and unidentifiable vegetables. Three quarters of the vegetable matter in Ötzi's intestines consists of well-chewed cereal which may have been eaten as bread. Charcoal and mineral particles in his intestines indicate that he prepared his last meal over an open fire and used flour ground in a stone mill.

POLLEN COUNT

To identify Ötzi's origins, the pollen in his stomach was of particular importance. Pollen is ingested both in food and by breathing in air. In Ötzi, the pollen came mainly from goosefoot, plane, hops, hazel and spruce. Hops are only abundant south of Alps. Due to the degree of digestion shown in the pollen, botanists believe that Ötzi must have been in the Venosta Valley twelve hours before his death. The types of wood Ötzi selected for making his tools indicate they came from a variety of mixed woodland typical of the Venosta and the Senales Vallies.

EVIDENCE OF A RELIGIOUS WORLD

Even in Ötzi's time many people believed in gods and spirits. Offerings were made beside statues or menhirs which resembled human beings. These life-size sculptures were probably holy to the people of the Stone Age. Skilled sculptors chiseled images of weapons, jewellery and clothes into these stones.

STONE PEOPLE

Male menhirs are principally decorated with weapons, above all daggers and axes. Female menhirs never depict weapons, only items of jewellery and can be recognised by images of breasts. There are also small neutral menhirs where only a necklace or a simple belt is to be seen, possibly representing children. Ötzi was probably familiar with the menhir on the far right, found in Lagundo, Italy in 1932.

THE REMEDELLO CULTURE

In Ötzi's time, along the edge of the Southern Alps and in the Alps of Lombardy, a tribe settled which manufactured exactly the same type of daggers, axes and arrowheads as we see among Ötzi's possessions. In particular, the find no. 102 from Remedello is comparable to Ötzi's equipment. The sculptor who made the menhirs of Lagundo and Laces knew the Remedello dagger and axe very well and chose them as models for his work.

Who was Ötzi?

Never before had an archaeological discovery created so much media interest. This time no treasure was found as when Heinrich Schliemann discovered the gold of Priamos in Troy or Howard Carter opened the tomb of Tutankhamen. Ötzi left a comparatively modest legacy behind. Is it the extraordinary location of the find which fascinates people? Is it Ötzi's facial expression which moves us or the distinctive posture of his arms? Or is it the personal fate of one man that we find so touching? The fact that the Iceman seems to have had his life taken away so suddenly makes us want to find out more about him and familiarize ourselves with the story of his life. Who was this man? What was he doing in this inhospitable terrain? What was his "profession"? So many answers are possible and each new assumption leads to further questions.

WAS ÖTZI AN OUTCAST?

It was first thought that Ötzi may have been driven out of his village and as a result found himself in those dangerous desolate heights. If he really were an outcast, why was he travelling along such a well-trodden path?

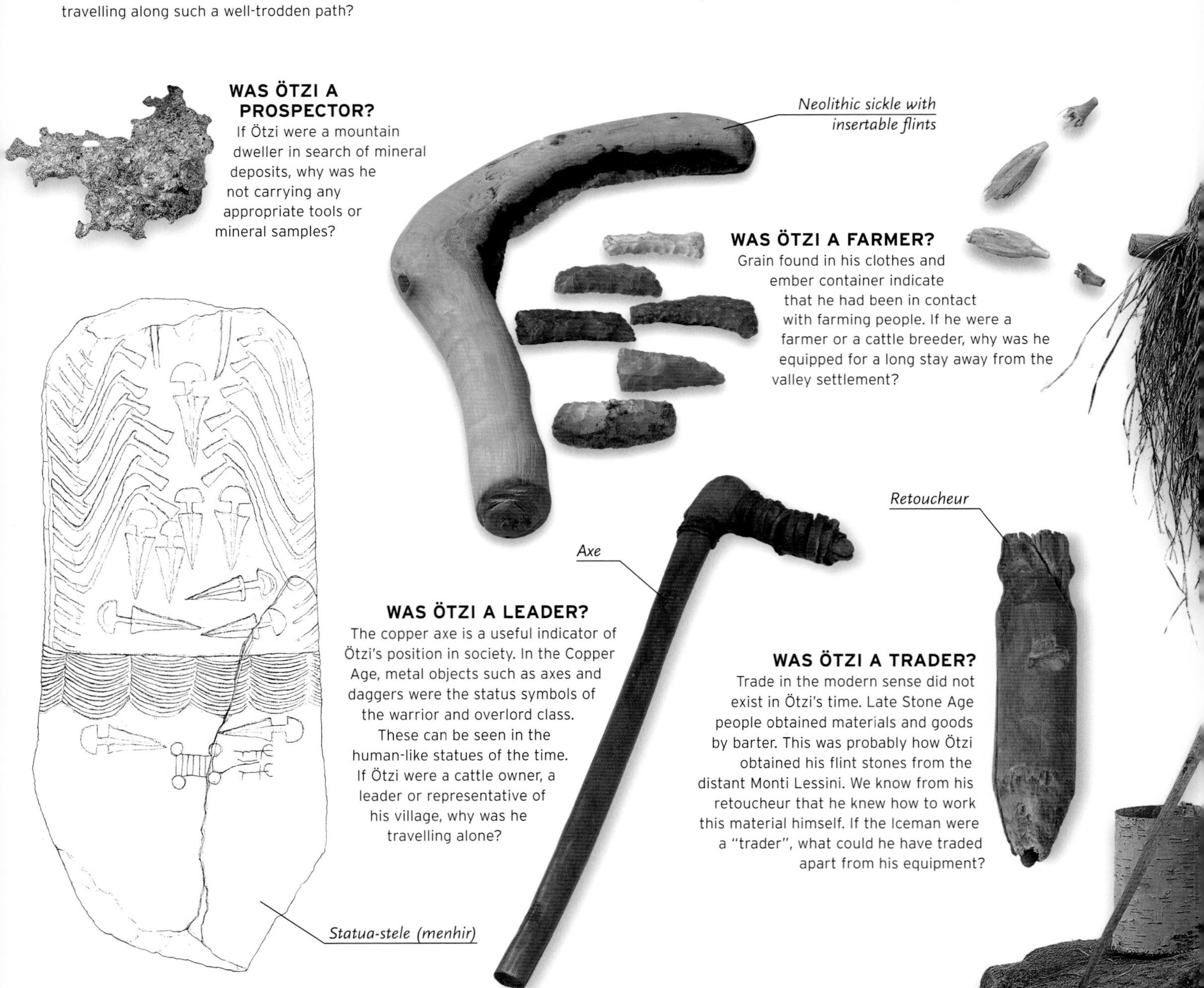

WAS ÖTZI A PROSPECTOR?

If Ötzi were a mountain dweller in search of mineral deposits, why was he not carrying any appropriate tools or mineral samples?

WAS ÖTZI A FARMER?

Grain found in his clothes and ember container indicate that he had been in contact with farming people. If he were a farmer or a cattle breeder, why was he equipped for a long stay away from the valley settlement?

WAS ÖTZI A LEADER?

The copper axe is a useful indicator of Ötzi's position in society. In the Copper Age, metal objects such as axes and daggers were the status symbols of the warrior and overlord class. These can be seen in the human-like statues of the time. If Ötzi were a cattle owner, a leader or representative of his village, why was he travelling alone?

WAS ÖTZI A TRADER?

Trade in the modern sense did not exist in Ötzi's time. Late Stone Age people obtained materials and goods by barter. This was probably how Ötzi obtained his flint stones from the distant Monti Lessini. We know from his retoucheur that he knew how to work this material himself. If the Iceman were a "trader", what could he have traded apart from his equipment?

WAS ÖTZI A HUNTER?

As well as the longbow and arrows, the remains of a net were found. Ötzi's flint tools could also be used for gutting and skinning hunted animals. If Ötzi were a hunter – and clearly he was – what was he doing up on a glacier without serviceable weapons?

Rough net for catching birds and rabbits

WAS ÖTZI A SHAMAN?

The only object among the Iceman's possessions whose use remains unknown is a hide tassel with a stone disc. A hide strap was threaded through a hole in the middle of the stone and through this loop, a further nine straps were attached. The tassel may have had a practical function but some people believe it is a piece of jewellery or a magical object belonging to a shaman. If Ötzi were a shaman, where were his priestly robes?

Stone disc

WAS ÖTZI A SHEPHERD?

In all probability, Ötzi was a wandering shepherd. The high pastures of the Upper Ötz Valley have been used for grazing since the Late Stone Age. Ötzi was well-equipped for long periods in high mountain territory. Making fires, finding food and repairing damaged tools are the daily chores of a wandering shepherd. However, if Ötzi were a shepherd, why were no traces of hair from sheep, goats or dogs found on him?

What or whoever the Iceman was, one thing is sure: he was skilled in a variety of crafts. He could make his own weapons and repair his tools and clothes, having the wisdom to select the most appropriate materials and use them to the best of his abilities.

Other Mummies

When a person dies, the body starts to decay. Slowly but surely, bacteria consume the body. Insects too can destroy a corpse. Finally only teeth and bones remain and these too gradually turn to dust. Many cultures used artificial methods such as embalming to protect their dead from decay. The best known mummies come from Egypt but in other parts of the world too, the art of mummification was practised. Furthermore, mummified corpses are still being discovered which were preserved without human assistance, simply because of their natural surroundings – in marshland, in the desert or in the ice.

JUANITA THE ICE MAIDEN
Four years after the discovery of Ötzi, the mummy of a fourteen-year-old Inca girl was found on the slopes of the Ampato volcano in the Peruvian Andes, 6,310 metres above sea level. She had been offered to the gods in a sacrifice and, after her death, wrapped in a beautiful shroud, tied in a bundle and buried in a grave. The dry, icy climate, just like a deep freezer, conserved her body, clothing and jewellery for over 500 years.

UNWRAPPED
The Chancay culture on the coast of Central Peru was renowned for its special art of weaving and pottery. Their dead were placed in a crouching position, bound in cloth or palm mats and dried in the sunshine. The mouth of this Chancay woman was stuffed with llama wool and closed with pieces of silver.

MUMMY BAGS
From the belt of this bound Chancay mummy hang small bags containing coca leaves, corn and medicinal plants. Coca leaves contain the substance used for making the drug cocaine.

"STUBSI": THE GLACIER CAT

Encouraged by the discovery of Ötzi, the summer of 1992 saw thousands of walkers searching the Alpine glaciers for further mummies. The only, rather modest, find in this particularly snowy year was a mummified cat which was found on the Schaufelferner in the Stubai Valley.

AN INUIT BABY

This Inuit child, found on a rugged mountain in Greenland in 1972, is over 500 years old. Lying protected from the sun and snow under a rocky outcrop, the body was freeze-dried by the icy Arctic air.

Piece of silver

CHEAP FUEL

Artificial mummification was practised in Ancient Egypt from about 2,600 years BC. By that time, Ötzi had already been dead for over 500 years. For over 3,000 years, a phenomenal number of human and animal bodies were embalmed. At the end of the 19th century, Egyptian steam trains used mummies to power their locomotives - they were the cheapest fuel available.

FAMILIAR FACE

The ancient Egyptians believed that people's souls lived on after their death and returned to their bodies every night. Therefore corpses had to be well-conserved and a human appearance maintained - the soul should be able to recognise the body. Mummies with portraits support this theory. The thin binding strips of this Egyptian mummy frame the upper section which contains a painted canvas with the head and shoulders of the mummified man.

Unbandaged mummy of an Egyptian boy

TRACES OF GOLD

The face of this bound Egyptian mummy was originally painted gold. The now visible teeth were covered in wax to keep the mouth closed. Both nostrils were blocked with stoppers, one of which has fallen out. Before the embalming commenced, the internal organs were removed by means of an incision in the stomach and the brain through the nose.

UNVEILED

Computer tomography makes it possible to see the contents of an Egyptian mummy without removing the coffin lid. Clearly visible is the conserving resin at the back of the skull, the binding around the face and the gold death mask at the front.

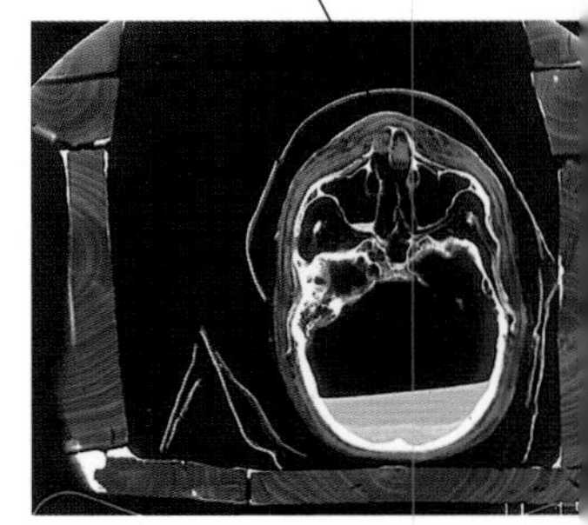

The resin introduced into the cranial fossa for conservation purposes is clearly visible as is the binding on the face and the gold maskat the front.

THE TOLLUND MAN

This peaceful looking mummy was found on the Tollund Marsh in Denmark in 1950. Over 2,000 years ago the man was strangled and thrown into the moor. Marshes have a low oxygen content and so putrefying bacteria could scarcely develop.

MUMMIFIED IN PERMAFROST

John Torrington was a crew member of the two ships captained by Franklin which set out in 1846 to find the North-West Passage. His icy grave and that of two other sailors were found in the Canadian Arctic - all the other crew members were lost without trace.

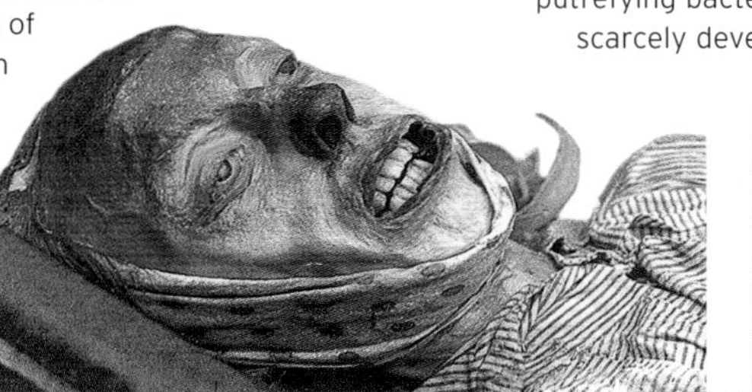

Ötzi in Bolzano

Wrapped in an operating gown and laid on crushed ice, Ötzi was conserved at the Anatomical Institute of Innsbruck University for six years. In January 1996, he returned south of the Alps, not far from where his last journey had been so rudely interrupted, to his final resting place: a magnificent building on the outskirts of Bolzano's historic centre housing the South Tyrol Museum of Archaeology. Here, in a space of 1,200 m^2 on four floors, the treasures of South Tyrolean history are on show. The first floor is entirely dedicated to the Copper Age and it is here that the Iceman lies in semi-darkness, brown and leathery, his eye sockets empty, his left arm noticeably twisted, exhibited for his descendants and heavily guarded. Visitors from the world over pass through, fascinated, astonished and strangely moved by the sight of a witness of our past.

LOOK OUT!
The South Tyrol Museum of Archaeology is guarded day and night. Video cameras and movement detectors are only a small part of the security system.

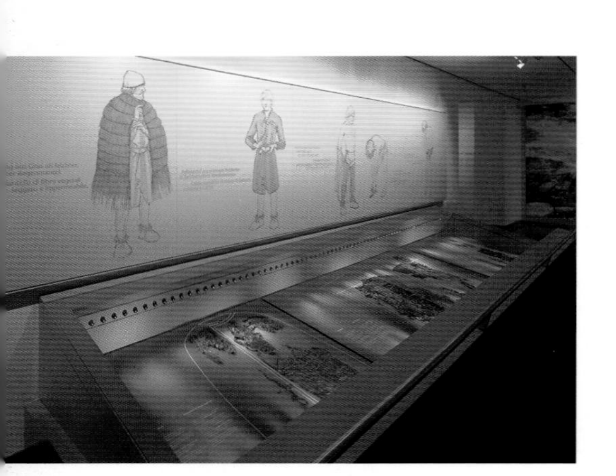

FIRST FLOOR
The original Iceman finds are displayed in special air-conditioned cabinets. Drawings in 1:1 scale highlight the craft skills of the Copper Age. Videos and interactive multi-media stations complete the exhibition, enabling visitors to get an impression of Ötzi's world and also the events of his discovery, recovery and medical examinations.

DELICATE OBJECTS
The finds in the cabinets are maintained at a constant temperature of 18° C and due to their sensitivity to light, are only illuminated at 50 lux. Leather objects are regularly greased.

EXPERIENCING ARCHAEOLOGY
Children and young people are very welcome visitors at the South Tyrol Museum of Archaeology. On the ground floor, a special activity centre has been set up for them where the staff help to bring history to life so that children can experience it close up. Young people get the chance to try out different handicrafts and make experiments of all kinds - pottery, grass weaving, stone carving and leather cutting - so that they become familiar with the way Ötzi's clothes looked and how he wore them and perhaps imagine themselves wandering along the Roman Road in a toga and tunic...

ELECTRONICALLY GUARDED

The EDP unit records all the values which the mummy and the cold chamber require: air pressure, temperature, relative humidity and even the mummy's weight. At the slightest variation, an alarm goes off and specialised technicians and a doctor can get to work.

COOL CLIMATE

In contrast to the other departments of the South Tyrol Museum of Archaeology, the Ötzi floor is kept in semi-darkness and heavily refrigerated. Thermo-hydrographs constantly control the room temperature and humidity.

HIGH-TECH FOR THE ICEMAN

To stop the Iceman from rotting, he must be kept in conditions similar to those which conserved him in the ice for over 5,000 years: freezing cold with high air humidity. An entirely new cooling device had to be developed so that the mummy could be displayed without protective covering or the use of crushed ice. This conservation system prevents a layer of ice from covering the mummy's body.

A GLIMPSE OF PREHISTORIC TIMES

The mummy can be seen through this small tank glass window. It lies on precision scales in a germ-free environment at a temperature of -6° C and 98% air humidity. A special filter removes both ultra-violet and infra-red rays from the light. This cell is only a small part of the whole Ötzi "suite". Out of bounds to visitors are the adjoining back-up cold chamber, an examination room, a disinfection room, a laboratory, an EDP unit and a machine and technology room.

Marketing Ötzi

An archaeological find of this importance offers succulent marketing opportunities. The souvenir industry immediately recognised Ötzi's potential as an advertising medium – after all, he had become one of the most famous personalities of the decade, almost on a par with Princess Diana. Cartoonists started to use his image and before long, he was being printed on postcards and T-shirts and even used as a mould for a new brand of jelly babies. Pop singers sang about him and he became the hero of numerous children's books. In short, business was booming. However, despite this commercial overkill, the enthusiasm so many of us feel for this Neolithic man who suddenly had his life taken away only to be later catapulted into our time, along with all his clothes and possessions, remains totally legitimate. His story managed to stun even our sensationalist world. Before the discovery of the Iceman, archaeologists were forced to reconstruct life in the past through the paltry remains of skeletons, graves and burial objects. The Iceman has changed all that.

Ötzi on a pizza – with olive fists and broccoli hair

Chronicle of Events and Timeline

THURSDAY,
SEPTEMBER 19, 1991
The German couple Simon discovered a brown figure partly emerging from the ice near the Hauslabjoch at 3,210 metres above sea level.

Later they reported their discovery at the nearby Similaun refuge. The owner informed the Austrian police in Sölden and the Italian carabinieri in Senales. He then set off for the Tisenjoch.

There the refuge owner saw the corpse and a mass of strange objects including wood, string, bunches of grass and scraps of hide.

FRIDAY,
SEPTEMBER 20
An Austrian recovery team arrived at the Hauslabjoch by helicopter and attempted to extract the corpse from the ice using a pneumatic drill. In the process the left hip and upper thigh were damaged. Finally the weather got worse and the recovery attempt was abandoned. A policeman took away the axe he had found on a rocky ledge and handed it in to the police in Sölden.

SATURDAY,
SEPTEMBER 21
The refuge owner's father unsuccessfully attempted to free the corpse. By chance the mountaineers Reinhold Messner and Hans Kammerlander happened to be in the area and visited the location of the find. Messner estimated the dead man to be at least 500 years old.

SUNDAY,
SEPTEMBER 22
The body was successfully removed and prepared for transport. The head of the Innsbruck recovery team was informed. On Sunday night however, temperatures dropped and the body froze in again.

MONDAY,
SEPTEMBER 23
Reporters from Austrian television arrived before the start of the official recovery attempt.

In front of the cameras, forensic doctors from Innsbruck University freed the corpse with the aid of a ski-stick and an ice axe.

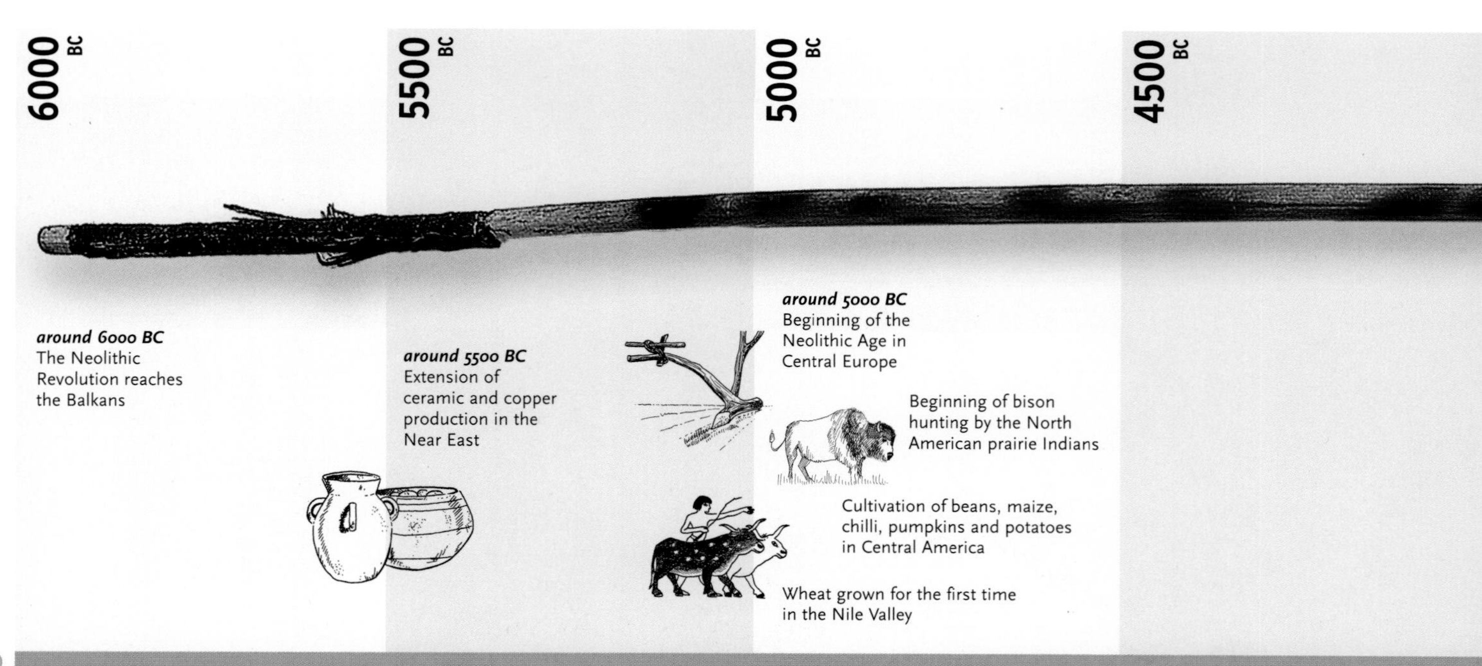

Items of the man's equipment were also dug up and stacked in a pile. They were packed into a body bag along with the corpse.

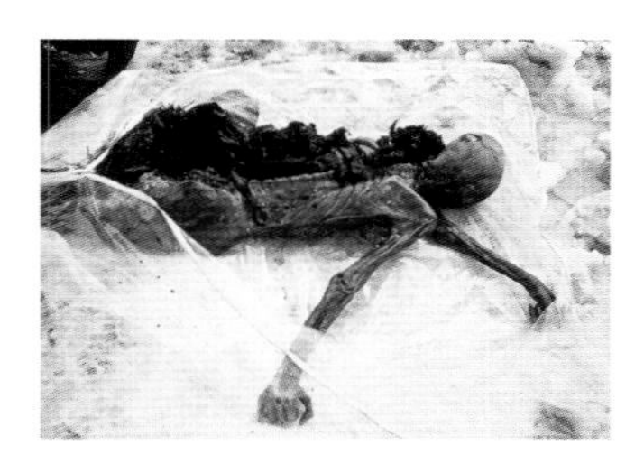

The corpse was flown by helicopter to the village of Vent in the Ötz Valley. There it was placed in a coffin and taken on to the Institute for Forensic Medicine in Innsbruck. On the way they stopped off in Sölden to pick up the axe.

TUESDAY, SEPTEMBER 24
Six days after its recovery, the corpse was finally examined by an archaeologist, Konrad Spindler, professor of Primeval and Early History at Innsbruck University (second from left). Spindler immediately recognised the great age and significance of the find. Crowds of journalists descended on the university buildings. Telephone calls came in from all over the world. That very evening the corpse was moved to a cold chamber in the neighbouring anatomical institute.

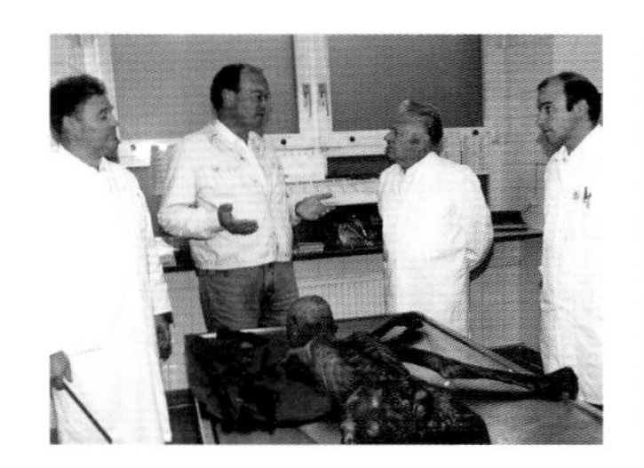

WEDNESDAY, SEPTEMBER 25
At the location of the find, experts discovered the mummy's quiver. An initial archaeological expedition was organised but bad weather forced it to be postponed. Meanwhile in Innsbruck, two restorers from the Römisch-Germanisches Zentralmuseum in Mainz, Germany, arrived in Austria to undertake the first preparatory steps towards the mummy's restoration.

THURSDAY, SEPTEMBER 26
A week after the find, the name "Ötzi" was used for the first time.

FRIDAY, SEPTEMBER 27
Archaeologists found a round piece of wood, a sloeberry, bunches of hay and scraps of leather. Heavy snowfalls prevented further digging. Rumours began to circulate that the location of the find was actually on Italian territory, not in Austria.

MONDAY, SEPTEMBER 30
In Vienna, talks began to discuss the place of restoration, further archaeological excavations and the foundation of a new research institute.

TUESDAY, OCTOBER 1
The location of the find and the artefacts were placed under official protection.

WEDNESDAY, OCTOBER 2
New surveys clearly established that Ötzi had been found on South Tyrolean terrain, in Italy. Originally it was thought that the find location, close to the border, was on the Austrian side as the waters of the Ötz Valley flow into the River Inn. According to the treaty of 1919, in which the South Tyrol became a part of Italy, the watershed was taken to represent the border between the two. At that time, the location of the find was covered in a twenty-metre-thick thick layer of snow so the actual border line could not be exactly established.

4000 BC

around 4000 BC
Megalithic burials in Western Europe

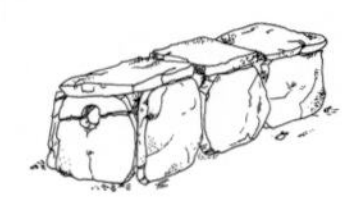

Settlement of Alaska by the Eskimos

3500 BC

around 3500 BC
Beginning of the Copper Age in Central Europe
Beginning of the Bronze Age in the Near East

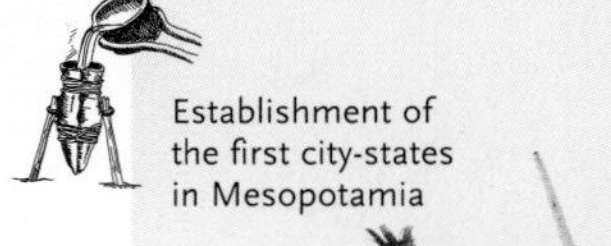

Establishment of the first city-states in Mesopotamia

from 3350-3100 BC
Ötzi, the Iceman, lived in the Alps

3000 BC

around 3000 BC
Unification of the Kingdom of Egypt under the first Egyptian Pharaoh Menes; development of hieroglyphics; cultivation of rice in China

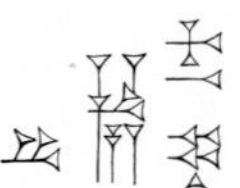

around 2900 BC
Development of cuneiform script in Mesopotamia; discovery of the wheel in Ancient Sumeria

around 2800 BC
Erection of the stone circle of Stonehenge in England

2500 BC

around 2500 BC
Construction of the Great Pyramid in Egypt under the Pharaoh Cheops

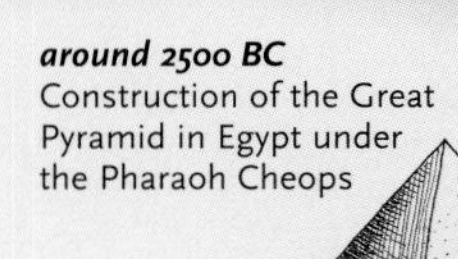

around 2300 BC
Beginning of the Bronze Age in Central Europe

THURSDAY, OCTOBER 3
Two delegations got underway. One accompanied the transfer of the finds to Mainz and the second headed to the Hauslabjoch to start the first archaeological excavations. On October 5 however, they were interrupted by further bad weather. For three days researchers melted the snow and ice with steam jets and blowers, revealing Ötzi's grass cape, further pieces of leather and hide belonging to his clothing, shreds of the two birch-bark containers and their contents, sections of a wide-meshed net, string, splinters of wood and two splintered ibex vertebrae.

JULY 20, 1992
Preparations began for the second archaeological excavation. After the heavy snowfalls of the winter 1991–92, 2 metres of snow had to be shovelled away. Actual archaeological work began on August 10 and lasted two weeks. Numerous small finds such as grasses, moss, leaves, pieces of charcoal, hairs, a fingernail and parts of insects were found. There were also more important finds such as the bearskin cap and the remaining section of the broken longbow which had remained anchored in the ice since the previous summer.

SEPTEMBER 1991 – JANUARY 1998
For the following three years and then extended until 1998, Innsbruck University was authorised by the South Tyrolean Government to hold on to the Iceman and organise a thorough research programme.

The Glacier Mummy remained in the cold chambers of the Institute for Anatomy for six years. The cold, damp conditions essential for the Iceman's conservation were created by means of multi-layered packaging consisting of a sterile operating gown, layers of crushed

ice, a plastic covering, an ice pack and cling film. Researching the Iceman is the sole objective of the newly-founded Research Institute for Alpine Prehistory.

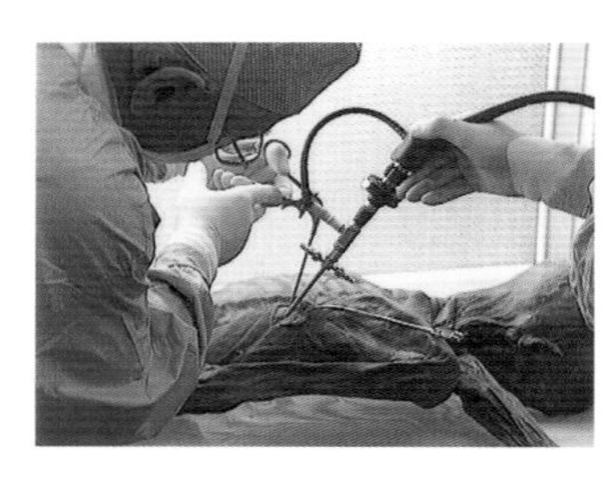

The results of six years of scientific research have made it possible to further reconstruct Ötzi's living conditions.

Over sixty international research teams are involved in Innsbruck University's research programme. Hair for example, is analysed at the Bundeskriminalamt in Wiesbaden, Germany and at the German Wool Research Institute in Aachen while Ötzi's fingernail was sent to Chieti in Central Italy.

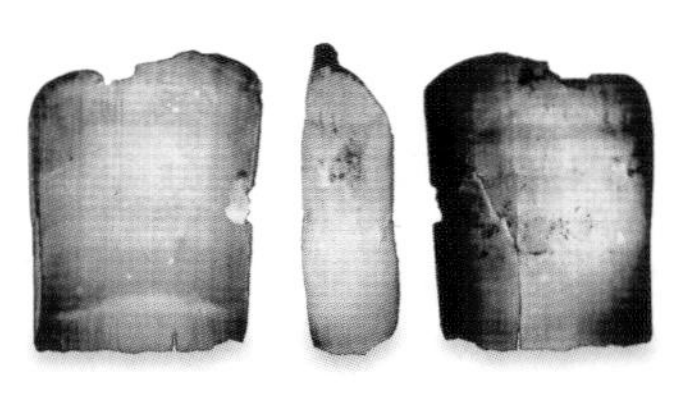

For over three years the finds were conserved and restored at the Römisch-Germanisches Zentralmuseum, Mainz. Among those who work in the laboratories and workshops of this prestigious museum are experts in the conservation of finds made of organic materials.

around 2000 BC
Indo-European migration
Palace Culture in Crete

around 1000 BC
First cities with temple-pyramids in Central Mexico;
Greek settlements on the coasts of Asia Minor;
Blooming of the Phoenician cities

around 500 BC
Persian Wars;
The Roman Republic;
Buddha founds his monastic order

around 400 BC
Classical Greece

around 300 BC
Alexander the Great conquers Egypt,
Rome achieves supremacy in Italy

SEPTEMBER 1995 – OCTOBER 1997

The unique find on the Hauslabjoch motivated the South Tyrolean Government to go ahead with the creation of the South Tyrol Museum of Archaeology which would form an appropriately prestigious home for the Glacier Mummy. A splendid building, formerly housing a bank, on the edge of Bolzano's historic centre was designated as Ötzi's final resting place.

JANUARY 16, 1998

Amid strict security precautions, Ötzi and the rest of the finds were moved from the Anatomical Institute of Innsbruck University to the new South Tyrol Museum of Archaeology in Bolzano.

The Provincial Governor of the South Tyrol, Luis Durnwalder, and two members of the Provincial parliament, Bruno Hosp and Alois Kofler, gave a press conference to inform of the successful transfer and the excellent working relationship with Innsbruck University. They also revealed that the regional authorities did not see Bolzano as merely the location of an Ötzi exhibition but rather a place where further scientific research and documentation would be encouraged.

MARCH 28, 1998

A ceremony was held to open the South Tyrol Museum of Archaeology. Its centrepiece is the small high-tech cold chamber in which Ötzi can be observed without protective covering or crushed ice. The setting is however dignified and respects the fact that this is Ötzi's resting place.

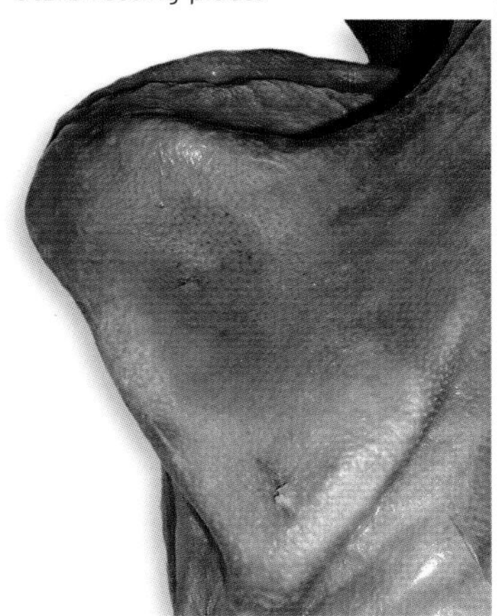

JUNE 2001

During a routine examination in Bolzano, an arrowhead was discovered in Ötzi's left shoulder. An important question relating to the fate of the glacier mummy was therefore cleared up: Ötzi was murdered.

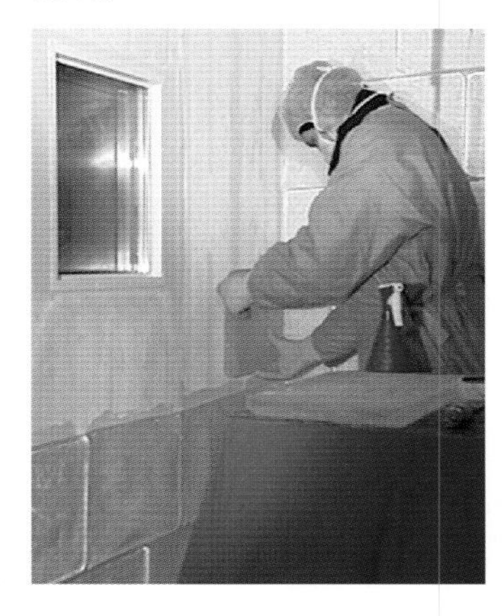

DECEMBER, 2003

Ötzi's cold chamber was converted into an "igloo". By lining the walls with plates of ice and installing a new lighting system and measuring instruments, optimum humidity can be better maintained than in the old cold chamber. In the past the mummy would lose five grams of water within 24 hours, requiring his corpse to be sprayed with sterilised water every two weeks in order to make up for this loss of humidity.

0 | **500 AD** | **1000 AD** | **1500 AD** | **Today**

around the birth of Christ
Roman conquest of Gaul and Egypt

around 200 AD
Expansion of Christianity

around 300 AD
Beginning of Aztec culture in Central Mexico; Classic Maya period in Southern Mexico

around 600 AD
Death of the Prophet Mohammed

around 700 AD
Extension of Islam into Egypt and Buddhism into Japan

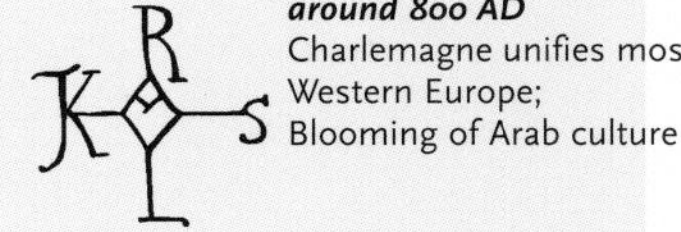

around 800 AD
Charlemagne unifies most of Western Europe; Blooming of Arab culture

around 1150 AD
The Crusades – Western European, Byzantine and Islamic cultures meet

around 1350 AD
Plague in Europe

around 1400
Beginning of the Italian Renaissance; construction of the Great Wall of China; rise of the Aztecs in Mexico and the Incas in Peru

1454
The Gutenberg Bible printed

1492
Columbus reaches America

around 1500
Reformation in Northern Europe

1789
French Revolution

1914–1918
First World War

1939–1945
Second World War

1969
First moon landing

Index

Photo Credits

t = top
c = centre
b = bottom
l = left
r = right

With the exception of those listed below, all the photography is the work of Augustin Ochsenreiter on behalf of the South Tyrol Museum of Archaeology.

Amt für Bodendenkmäler der Autonomen Provinz Bozen-Südtirol: 7 t, 8 bc, 9 tr, 10 bl, 10 cl, 10-11 tc, 11 tl, 11c, 11 cr, 45 tl, 60/1 b, 62/2
Bundeskriminalamt Wiesbaden (K. Kramer) 10 bcr, 13 c, 62/4 t
Rolf Barth: 22 c
Folio Verlag
• no.parking: 6 bl, 8 t, 43 tr
• Othmar Seehauser: 61/4 b, 49 t
• Gudrun Sulzenbacher: 6 tl
Stefan Galler, Universität Salzburg: 14 bl
Greenland National Museum, Nuuk: 55 tr
Rainer Gothe/Heidrun Schöl, München: 13 tl
Gerlinde Haid: 8 cl, 60/2 b
Institut für Röntgendiagnostik und Nuklearmedizin, Klinikum Konstanz (A. Beck): 54 tcr
Landesgendarmeriekommando für Tirol: 7 cl, 9 c, 44 cl, 45 tc, 60/1 t, 60/2 t
Madison Press (Jack McMaster): 49 tl-cl
Ministero Beni Culturali Chieti: 50 t
Musei civici di Reggio Emilia (Virgilio Artioli): 51 bl
Museo Archeologico Nazionale, Chieti (Luigi Capasso): 10 c, 12 cr, 48 bcl, 62/4b
Musée de l'Homme, Paris: 54 c, 54 bl,
Werner Nosko: 61/2 t
Johan Reinhard: 55 cl
Jean-Loup Ringot 39 tr
Römisch-Germanisches Zentralmuseum, Mainz: 11 tr, 20 bc, 20 tl, 23 tcr, 26 cl, 36 tl, 44 bl, 62/1, 63/1 t
Römisch-Germanisches Zentralmuseum, Mainz/no.parking: 18 cr, 21 br
Renate Rolle, Hamburg (nach Artamonov): 16 bl
Servizio antropologico del Ministero Beni Culturale, Chieti: 13 br
Silkeborg Museum, Hovedgaarden, Silkeborg: 55 br
Südtiroler Archäologiemuseum: 48 t, 48 cl
• Gruppe Gut: 17 c, 52 bl
• Johanna and Katherina Putzer: 42 tl, timeline drawings
• Josef Pernter: 57 b, 63/1 b, 63/4 t
• Marco Samadelli: 50 tl, 52 tl, 61/4 t, 62/3 t, 63/4
• Othmar Seehauser: 6 cl, 50-51 c, 63/2
• Sara Welponer/no.parking: 10 t, 20 t, 21 tc, 21 tl, 21 cl, 22 cl, 23 bl, 24 bl, 30 cl, 31 bc, 32 tl, 38 tc, 40 tl, 40 tcl, 40 cl, 40 bcl, 42 cr, 53 br
Universität Innsbruck: 8 cr, 12 bl, 13 cl, 44 tl, 55 tl, 61/1 t, 62/3 b
• Helmuth Maurer: 15 tl, 15 tr, 15 c, 15 cl
• Klaus Oeggl: 9 tc
• Dieter zur Nedden: 13 tr, 14 t, 14 cl, 14 cr, 49 bl
Universität Leipzig, Ägyptologisches Museum (Karl Heinz von Stülpnagel): 54 c, 54 cl, 54 bc
University of Alberta (Owen Beattie): 54 bc
Uno Press: 60/3 b
Vienna Report: 8 bl, 9 br, 60/4